National Research Council. Committee on Science and Public Policy. Panel on Astronomical Facilities.

GROUND-BASED ASTRONOMY
A TEN-YEAR PROGRAM

A REPORT PREPARED BY THE PANEL ON ASTRONOMICAL FACILITIES
FOR THE COMMITTEE ON SCIENCE AND PUBLIC POLICY
OF THE NATIONAL ACADEMY OF SCIENCES

NATIONAL ACADEMY OF SCIENCES–NATIONAL RESEARCH COUNCIL
WASHINGTON, D.C. 1964

Endsheet: A portion of the Network Nebula in Cygnus, photographed with the 48-inch Schmidt telescope of the Mount Wilson and Palomar Observatories. The loop structure is composed of the debris of a supernova explosion many thousands of years ago. Radio telescopes detect the strongest radiation from the center of the loop.

Library of Congress catalog number 64-62266
Publication Number 1234

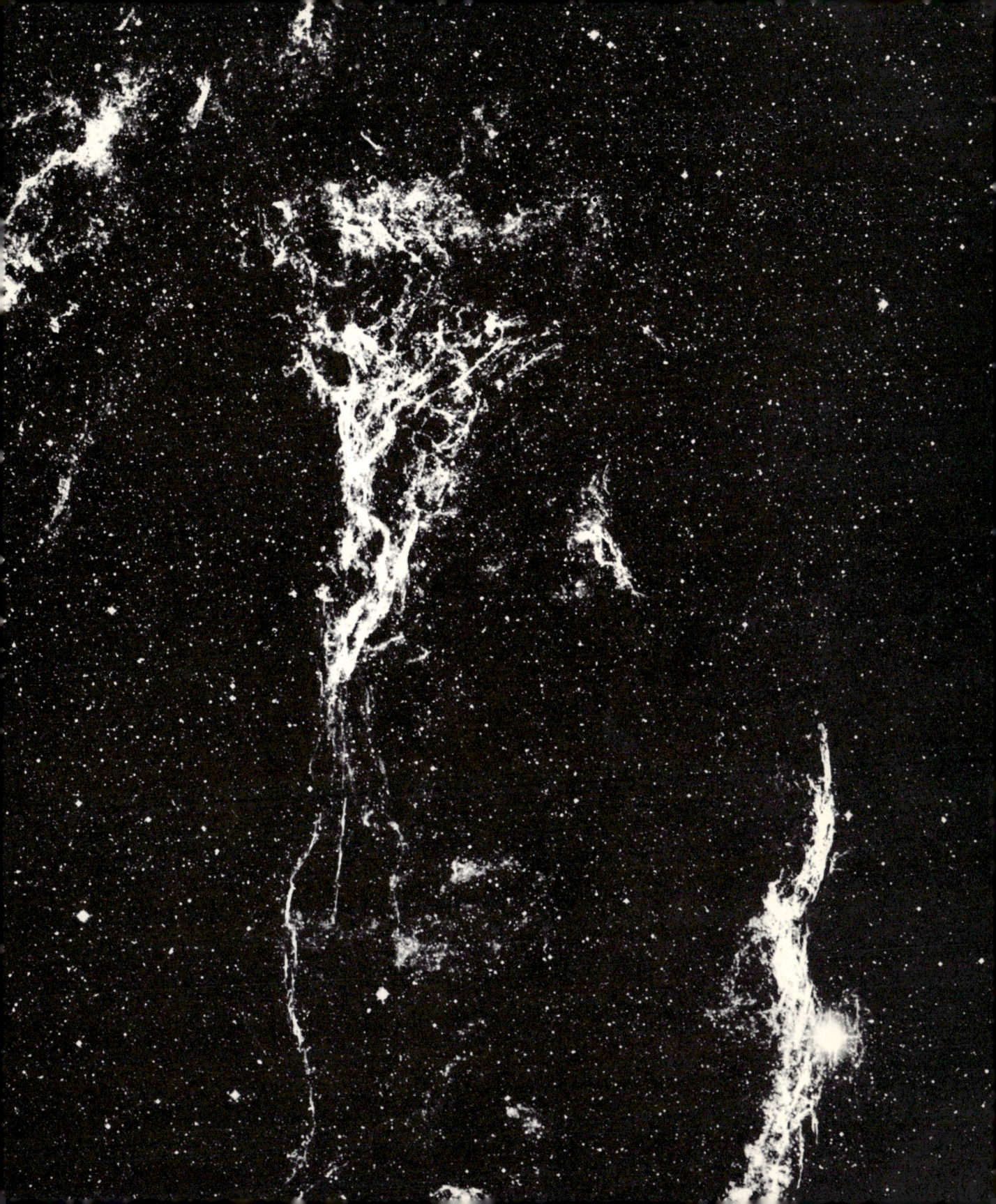

August 19, 1964

Dear Dr. Seitz:

The Committee on Science and Public Policy, on the basis of careful study of this report and extensive discussion with its authors, is pleased to endorse it to you for transmittal.

The report deals with ground-based astronomical facilities exclusively. It recommends certain new facilities, to be acquired at a rate based on an internal criterion—a conservative estimate of the rate at which astronomical progress can be made. We believe that this is the right approach to be adopted by panels of experts preparing "planning" reports, i.e., reports on the opportunities and needs of various fields of science. Determination of the optimum balance of the sciences as well as the over-all rate of scientific progress needed for achieving national goals requires many authoritative inputs of information relating to the various sciences, and the judgment of people concerned with national policies. We are convinced that the present report constitutes a very sound input for such determination.

The report presents an excellently balanced program for new facilities of ground-based astronomy in the next decade, well justified by the important scientific opportunities briefly discussed in the report. The care with which radio and optical programs have been interwoven and the selection of facilities at various levels to suit the expected spectrum of research and teaching activities are especially noteworthy. A good deal of care appears also to have gone into the consideration of the individual items of the program.

With regard to radioastronomical facilities, the Committee on Science and Public Policy is aware that in the past some substantially low cost estimates have been made, even by expert astronomical engineers. The situation has improved in recent years, however, and several major facilities (a 300-foot dish telescope, new 85-foot dishes, and some millimeter wave telescopes) have been completed at costs within a few percentage points of the original estimates. A great deal of care went into the cost estimates of the facilities proposed here, and we have no grounds to question the resultant figures. Some of these facilities are quite advanced, however, and we join the authors of the report in recommending that further detailed cost estimates be undertaken prior to decisions involving such facilities. The total scope of the facilities program appears very reasonable and well justified by the promises of radio astronomy.

With regard to optical facilities we find that the recommended plan is definitely conservative. In fact, if we have any doubts at all, it is that it may err on the side of conservatism by not providing sufficient opportunities for the growing number of young astronomers at the graduate level and slightly beyond to make use of first-class research facilities. We are also not sure that the proposed facilities and supporting instrumentation, which clearly require rapid development, would be adequate to permit their effective use by groups closely related to astronomy and yet not quite an integral part of it. We mean, for instance, scientists who are concerned with the details of planetary structure and composition.

The Panel that prepared this report was requested to concern itself primarily with astronomical facilities. The report, however, includes a brief section in which estimates of the annual costs of scientific activities, which are additive to the costs of facilities and their maintenance, are presented. The Panel's study of this subject was considerably less detailed than its study of facilities requirements, but we believe that the findings are quite reasonable and are consistent with the proposed plan for facilities.

The report rightly emphasizes astronomy as a pure science. Its sweep and grandeur have had an inner fascination for all people at all times and is certain to have it in the future. We would be remiss if we did not note with the Panel the major contributions of astronomy to other sciences—for example, the discovery of helium and the contributions to the problem of thermonuclear reactions.

Clearly the federal agency whose activities will be most directly affected by research with the help of new astronomical facilties is the National Aeronautics and Space Administration. The connection between the subject matter of the National Aeronautics and Space Administration's interest and the interests of ground-based astronomy is close, not only in the well-recognized problems of the solar system, but in the equally exciting areas of interstellar particles and fields, ultraviolet radiation of the stars, and radio, X-ray, and gamma-ray energy sources. The National Aeronautics and Space Administration is, in fact, engaged in all these fields with its orbiting experiments. The nation's newly gained technology of extraterrestrial astronomy makes it imperative that the knowledge that can be had from the ground in these areas be pushed ahead as fast as possible so that the space effort will have the strongest possible back-up. A move by the National Aeronautics and Space Administration to broaden its already strong interest in basic astronomical research so as to include ground-based stellar astronomy would be highly advantageous to the national scientific effort and to the National Aeronautics and Space Administration itself. The keen and well-justified interest of the National Aeronautics and Space Administration in the training of space scientists could well be extended to assistance and increase in facilities for all astronomy, because the space and ground-based activities of astronomers are but the two faces of the same coin.

The National Science Foundation has given the broadest possible support to research in astronomy; the Foundation and the Office of Naval Research have been the principal channels for Federal participation in the support of this research. It is essential that the broad support from these sources, which constitutes so vital a contribution to the advancement of astronomy, be continued. The National Science Foundation and the Office of Naval Research, together with the National Aeronautics and Space Administration, could form a strong government team that would carry astronomy forward on all fronts, by means of a balanced program of support of all elements along the lines envisioned in this report.

In conclusion, we wish to recommend a careful study of this report and the adoption of its recommendations to those who are concerned with federal planning of support of science; it is a carefully prepared and well-conceived document. We extend our compliments on a job well done to all those who participated in its preparation, and especially to the chairman and members of the Panel, who devoted major personal effort to this report.

Sincerely yours,
G. B. Kistiakowsky

FOR THE COMMITTEE ON SCIENCE AND PUBLIC POLICY

Since its founding in 1863, the Academy has had a deep interest in ground-based astronomy. Benjamin A. Gould, a charter member of the Academy, was an internationally famous astronomer of his day. George Ellery Hale, the first chairman of the National Research Council, was enormously effective in advancing astronomy in our country to a leading position in world astronomy.

In continuation of this interest the Academy's Committee on Science and Public Policy undertook a study of the need for facilities in this field. It is a privilege to make their work known.

Frederick Seitz
PRESIDENT
NATIONAL ACADEMY OF SCIENCES

Washington, D.C.
August 25, 1964

PANEL ON ASTRONOMICAL FACILITIES

A. E. Whitford, Chairman, Lick Observatory, University of California
R. N. Bracewell, Radio Astronomy Institute—Radioscience Laboratory, Stanford University
Frank D. Drake, Department of Astronomy, Cornell University
Frederick T. Haddock, Jr., Radio Astronomy Observatory, University of Michigan
William Liller, Department of Astronomy, Harvard University
W. W. Morgan, Yerkes Observatory, University of Chicago
Bruce H. Rule, California Institute of Technology
Allan R. Sandage, Mt. Wilson and Palomar Observatories, California Institute of Technology, Carnegie Institution of Washington

COMMITTEE ON SCIENCE AND PUBLIC POLICY

George B. Kistiakowsky, Harvard University, Chairman
Lawrence R. Blinks, Stanford University
H. W. Bode, Bell Telephone Laboratories
Frank Brink, Jr., The Rockefeller Institute
Melvin Calvin, University of California
Frank L. Horsfall, Jr., Sloan-Kettering Institute for Cancer Research
A. L. Lehninger, The Johns Hopkins University
Saunders Mac Lane, University of Chicago
Carl Pfaffmann, Brown University
Allan R. Sandage, Mount Wilson and Palomar Observatories
Harry L. Shapiro, American Museum of Natural History
T. M. Sonneborn, Indiana University
John Verhoogen, University of California
Alvin M. Weinberg, Oak Ridge National Laboratory
Robert E. Green, National Academy of Sciences, Executive Secretary

FOREWORD

The Panel on Astronomical Facilities was established late in 1962 by the National Academy of Sciences as an activity of the Academy's Committee on Science and Public Policy. The established purpose of the Panel was to study the probable need for major new astronomical facilities in the United States during the next five to ten years, and to recommend guiding principles and estimates of cost in order that federal funds might be employed with maximum efficiency to promote advancement of astronomy in all its branches. The members of the Panel, chosen to be representative of the most active groups in both optical and radio astronomy, have attempted to assess the direction that the observational branch of the science is likely to take in the decade ahead, and to recommend a program of facilities that will build upon the strength and productivity that the American astronomical community has already demonstrated.

The study was confined to ground-based facilities. Investigations of the universe by telescopes carried above the earth's atmosphere are under the cognizance of review bodies considering various aspects of the national space program, and the Panel has not considered them to be within its stated purview. It has, however, given thought to the relative roles of orbiting and ground-based telescopes and to the proper division of tasks between the two methods of observation, in order to appraise any imbalance in support or emphasis that may exist. The Panel has been guided by the view that astronomy is a branch of the physical sciences engaged in basic research of the purest sort, traditionally motivated by the desire to know and understand. It is true that astronomy has also provided economic or practical dividends such as navigation, guidance systems, and the gathering of data that guide and support the national space program. Furthermore, astronomy has enriched all other sciences: examples are the discovery of the element helium from observations of the sun; the recognition of thermonuclear reactions as a source of energy and as an explanation of the origin of the elements; and development of a picture of the early history of the earth—important to both geology and biology. Nevertheless, the Panel has considered its assignment to be the formulation of a facilities program dictated by the orderly development of observational astronomy as a pure science, not tied to mission-oriented facilities that may be provided with other goals in mind.

The Panel has sought to arrive at a set of recommendations that will be reasonable and prudent, consistent with growth rates already established. The Panel has felt, however, that these rational precautions should be secondary to its main charge: to recommend ground-based instruments that will enable astronomers to exploit the opportunities that beckon—both age-old problems that are on the verge of yielding to observational attack and exciting new developments of transcendent importance.

The support that the federal government gives to such a program is in the same category as that given to investigations of the interior of the earth, of the depths of the ocean, of the upper atmosphere, and indeed to the exploration of space by orbiting vehicles. These efforts are all consequences of the natural human desire to understand the larger aspects of man's environment. To the non-specialist the far reaches of space and time investigated by the astronomer have widespread appeal. The Panel believes that an investment in ground-based astronomical facilities of the order of one half of 1 per cent of that going into the space effort would be consistent with a balanced program of federal support for science.

CONTENTS

I   INTRODUCTION AND GENERAL STATEMENT   1

The Nature of Astronomy   1

Development of a World Picture   1

Role of the United States in Astronomical Research   3
    Optical Astronomy   3
    Radio Astronomy   4

Current Problems   5
    Creation of the Chemical Elements   6
    New Knowledge from Radio Astronomy   6
    Exploding Galaxies   6
    Quasi-Stellar Radio Sources   8

The Inadequacy of Present Facilities   9

The Relation of Ground-Based and Space Astronomy   10

II   THE PRESENT POSITION IN GROUND-BASED ASTRONOMY   13

Theoretical Astrophysics   13

Optical Astronomy   14
    Present Dominant Position of the United States   14
    The Limiting Factor for Future Success   15

Radio Astronomy   18
    Present Position of the United States   18
    Need for High Angular Resolution   18
    Resolution of Radio Galaxies   19
    Resolution and the Cosmological Problem   20
    Methods of Achieving High Angular Resolution   21
    Collecting Area and Sidelobes as Limiting Factors   23
    Parabolic Antennas   24

The Dilemma of the Astronomy Graduate School in 1964   26

Manpower   28
- *Training of Astronomers Compared to Training of Other Physical Scientists*   29
- *U. S. Membership in the International Astronomical Union*   31
- *Graduate Student Population in Astronomy Departments*   32
- *A Ten-Year Projection*   35
- *Conclusion*   37

III   A PROGRAM FOR CONSTRUCTION OF OPTICAL TELESCOPES   38

Types Needed   38
- *Special-Purpose Telescopes*   39
- *Solar Telescopes*   39

Size Categories   40

Performance versus Size   40

How Big?   42

Large Telescopes   42

Location of Large Telescopes   43

Under What Auspices?   44
- *Previous Performance*   44
- *Type of Institution*   44
- *The Primary Goal*   46

Engineering Study for a Giant Telescope   46

Telescopes of Moderate Size   47

Small Telescopes   48

Summary of Recommendations for Optical Telescopes   49

IV   A PROGRAM FOR CONSTRUCTION OF RADIO TELESCOPES   50

A Major High-Resolution Instrument   50

A High-Resolution Array of Limited Capability   52

Large Paraboloids   53

Smaller Special-Purpose Instruments   54

Design Study for the Largest Possible Steerable Paraboloid   56

A Solar Radar System 57
Summary of Recommendations for Radio Telescopes 57

V   AUXILIARY INSTRUMENTS AND AUTOMATION 58

Auxiliary Instruments 58
    Radiation Detectors 59
    Auxiliary Optical Instruments 60
    Atmospheric Disturbances 61
    Recommendations 62

Automation 63
    Introduction 63
    Acquisition and Reduction of Data 64
    Development of New Automatic Instruments 65
    Information Storage 66
    Automated Observatories 67
    Recommendations 68

VI   THE MAGNITUDE OF THE PROGRAM 71

Introduction 71

Summary of Recommendations and Costs 74
    Optical Astronomy 74
    Radio Astronomy 75
    Auxiliary Instruments and Automation 75
    Annual Operating Support 76

Basis of Cost Estimates and Projected Spending Rate 76
    Facility Cost Estimates 76
    Annual Operating Support for New Facilities 80
    Spending Rate 83
    Annual Scientific Support for Existing Facilities 87

APPENDIX 88

1 INTRODUCTION AND GENERAL STATEMENT

THE NATURE OF ASTRONOMY

Astronomy has as its domain the study of the celestial bodies—the sun, planets, stars, clouds of gas between the stars, galaxies—and indeed the entire universe considered as a single system. Astronomy's goal is to learn the nature of these diverse objects and to relate their properties, their motions, and their distribution in space in a unified world picture; to understand the evolutionary development of the universe from the time of its formation to the present epoch of observation and beyond; and indeed, to discover, if possible, its original state and its final destiny.

Unlike other sciences, where subtle and detailed experimentation can be done under controlled conditions in the laboratory, astronomy must be content to study the experiments that nature herself makes, "performed" in space by natural causes under uncontrolled conditions. All knowledge must be gleaned from the radiation coming from the objects under study. Although this transfer link is a feeble one, the light beams carry an amazing amount of information. Interpretation of the data using the laws of physics as we know them (dynamics, atomic and nuclear physics, thermodynamics, plasma physics) has produced our present understanding of the external universe.

DEVELOPMENT OF A WORLD PICTURE

Astronomy is the oldest of the sciences. As soon as man could write, he preserved his thoughts and speculations about the universe around him on cuneiform clay tablets, on papyrus, and in the Greek and Arabic documents that form our heritage. Ancient man observed the daily rising and setting of the sun, its annual journey northward and southward which produced the seasons, the phases of the moon, and the wandering of the planets against the background of the "fixed" stars. These regularities of the cosmos caused much wonder, and out of speculation arose those systems of cosmology with which the history of astronomy is written. In the early days of civilization, astronomy had a major role in forming man's concepts of his place in space and time.

Primarily as a result of discoveries by Aristarchus, by Ptolemy, by Copernicus, Galileo, Tycho, Kepler, and Newton, man's view of nature passed through a long series of profound revolutions. Early man naturally considered the earth to be the center of the universe—the fixed stars, the planets, and the sun being creations of the gods or even gods themselves. When regularities within the system were discovered, the geocentric theory with its crystalline spheres and epicycles was invented to explain the motions. This theory culminated in the Ptolemaic geocentric tables of planetary configurations. Unexplained discrepancies led certain visionaries to consider the sun rather than the earth to be the center of the world, but this hypothesis was so foreign to the ancient mind that not until the middle of the 16th century did Copernicus force a recognition of a heliocentric universe. The transition was so painful that Giordano Bruno lost his life for teaching it and Galileo was forced to recant his belief before the Church in Rome. But with the discoveries of the laws of planetary motion by Kepler and Newton, the revolution was complete.

In modern times, an equally profound transition has occurred with the recognition that the sun, with its planets, is one of a million million other stars comprising a large, flattened, slowly rotating system called the Milky Way galaxy. In turn, our galaxy, as a member of a local cluster of nearby galaxies, is but one of billions of other galaxies that make up the universe. And, in a discovery of deepest significance, the entire system has been found to be in a state of rapid expansion, each galaxy receding from every other.

Less than 50 years have passed since this world picture, with the atoms ordered into stars, stars into galaxies, galaxies into clusters, and clusters embedded in expanding space, was established with certainty from observations with the large telescopes constructed within this century. No armchair speculation could have conjured up such a hierarchy of systems to bring order out of apparent chaos. Yet nature, in some way yet dimly appreciated, has fashioned herself into such a pattern. Can we hope to learn how or when? Can we comprehend this structure as a sequence of events, each understandable in itself, unfolding in time? In the broadest sense this is the purpose of research in astronomy. Detailed projects on a multitude of subjects are leading, each in its own way, toward this goal.

Knowledge that seemed impossible to obtain 50 years ago is now either routinely known or can be found with our present capabilities. Today some of the deepest problems of astronomy and cosmology appear to be on the verge of yielding. We know the distances to stars, their sizes, surface temperatures, and the abundances of the chemical elements that comprise their surface layers. We know their space motions within the galaxy, their ages, their evolutionary history, and their probable fate. But there are many things we don't know. How are stars formed? Why do they condense from the interstellar medium into double, triple, and multiple systems that revolve around each other in gravitationally stable configurations? Why do some possess strong magnetic fields while others do not? How did the galaxies come into existence? What is the origin of radio signals from stars and galaxies? What is the origin of cosmic rays, and what are the nuclear processes that give rise to the high-energy gamma rays and X-rays that space probes are just beginning to observe? Perhaps the most fundamental question of all concerns the origin of the large-scale ordered magnetic fields that recent studies in radio astronomy have found to exist in certain regions of space.

Answers to some of these questions will undoubtedly come within the next decade; others, now only dimly perceived through the mists of present ignorance, must wait until our present knowledge can be broadened. Progress will be made by clever and aggressive use of telescopes of the largest size, equipped with detectors such as radio receivers, spectrographs, photometers, and photographic plates—instruments that analyze the faint incoming radiation made feeble by the enormous spreading out that has taken place in its long journey from its place of origin to the earth.

ROLE OF THE UNITED STATES IN ASTRONOMICAL RESEARCH

Optical Astronomy

Since 1900, the United States has held a dominant position in much of observational astronomy. The discoveries from which the present world picture has emerged have almost invariably come from observatories in this country. This was no accident; it came about between 1900 and 1950, solely because a few aggressive, inspired, and imaginative men in this country secured private funds to design and build the large telescopes with which the present frontier position in astrophysics was reached. Without these instruments, built in a period when government support did not exist, the knowledge we have today would have been denied us. The first systematic study of the distances to nearby stars could begin in America in the early 1900's with the long-focal-length refractors at the Allegheny Observatory (Pittsburgh), at the Yerkes Observatory (Chicago), at the Sproul Observatory (Swarthmore), at the Van Vleck Observatory (Connecticut Wesleyan), and several others—because these large telescopes existed. The discovery of the form of our galaxy in 1915 as a highly flattened rotating disk of stars, with the sun and its attendant planets at a peripheral position 30,000 light years from its center, would not have been possible without the 60-inch reflector on Mount Wilson. The discovery of the true nature of the external galaxies as separate "island universes" was possible in 1924 because the 36-inch Crossley reflector of the Lick Observatory and the 60-inch and 100-inch telescopes of Mount Wilson were available. And the expansion of the universe could be found in 1929 and studied adequately from 1929 to 1938 only with the 100-inch and 36-inch Crossley reflectors and their effective nebular spectrographs. Without this progression of instruments of increasing size, equipped with detectors of high sensitivity and sophistication, astrophysics would yet be largely in an infant state.

Radio Astronomy

In the new science of radio astronomy, it was the pioneer discoveries of young American scientists in the 1930's that opened up the field. The fundamental discovery came in 1931, when Karl G. Jansky of the Bell Telephone Laboratories found that radio waves were arriving from space at an intensity level a million million times greater than could be explained by the known properties of astronomical bodies. In the late 1930's the radio amateur Grote Reber surveyed the heavens with a 32-foot paraboloid erected in his back yard in Wheaton, Illinois, and produced the first coarse map of the radio sky. These promising beginnings were followed up, however, by bold developments in other countries, and the U. S. position over the past 15 years of rapid growth has not been dominant.

In the postwar years, it was the highly talented European and Australian scientists, rather than the Americans, who advanced radio astronomy by adapting wartime electronic developments to the observation of radio-frequency radiation from extraterrestrial objects. Discrete radio sources were soon discovered, and a treasure trove was opened up. Large radio telescopes and antenna arrays were built in Australia, England, and the Netherlands, and the United States fell far behind.

Serious U. S. efforts in radio astronomy began in the early 1950's with modest projects at the Naval Research Laboratory, where the first 50-foot paraboloid was built, and at Cornell University. A major discovery came in 1951 when the 21-centimeter radiation of hydrogen was detected by H. I. Ewen and E. M. Purcell at Harvard. Other important U. S. contributions included the discovery of powerful sporadic radio emissions from Jupiter and the development of the low-noise maser-type radio receiver.

A radio astronomy project at Harvard, started in 1953, produced the first Ph.D.'s in radio astronomy. Since 1955, developments at several universities, aided by enlightened federal support, have done much to regain the ground lost while other countries were surging ahead. The National Radio Astronomy Observatory, planned in 1954, is fulfilling its objective of providing radio astronomers from any part of the country with instruments beyond the capability of a single university; its 300-foot transit-mounted paraboloid considerably extends the capabilities of 60- to 90-foot paraboloids available at several universities. Very recently, the completion of a 1,000-foot, limited-coverage, fixed-mirror radio telescope at Arecibo, Puerto Rico (operated by Cornell University), has given the United States a preeminent position in radio astronomy with single-mirror antenna systems.

The United States now plays an important role in nearly all aspects of radio astronomy, and in a few fields, such as planetary physics, it is in a dominant position. In the use of extended antenna arrays to achieve high angular resolution, however, the United States is deficient. World-wide competition in radio astronomy is intense, and if the United States is to keep pace with progress elsewhere, and to realize the fruits of a revolutionary development that began on its own soil, the country must mount a diversified and far-reaching program.

CURRENT PROBLEMS

A brief survey of recent progress in aspects of astronomical research of great current interest demonstrates the important role played by large instruments:

Creation of the Chemical Elements

An important development in astronomy during the 1950's has been the spectrographic discovery that the abundance of heavy chemical elements in stellar atmospheres varies from star to star and is related to stellar age. This fact strongly suggests that the elements are continuously manufactured in the stars themselves under conditions of high temperature and pressure, and are distributed by stellar explosions throughout the interstellar medium in which new stars are formed. Here we have the strongest link between the large-scale world of astronomy and the subatomic world of nuclear physics, because we see that the origin of atomic nuclei is tied directly to the astronomical events in outer space. The data would not have been obtained without the use of large telescopes equipped with modern spectrographs.

New Knowledge from Radio Astronomy

Some of the great advances of the last 15 years have come through the application of radio astronomy methods. In this brief period, new and previously unsuspected phenomena have been found by radio techniques, phenomena that are now changing old concepts and enlarging our view of others. No portion of the observable universe has been left untouched by the effects of radio observations; our knowledge concerning the sun, the moon, the planetary system, our galaxy, and distant galaxies has been vastly increased.

In particular, the methods of radio astronomy have brought us a diversity of new knowledge—an improved distance to the sun, the configuration of the magnetic field of Jupiter, the temperature and structure of the invisible surface of Venus, the composition and roughness of the lunar surface, the temperature of the solar corona, the density distribution of neutral hydrogen in our galaxy, and a more complete picture of the rotation of our galaxy.

Radio astronomy studies today play key roles in all aspects of the study of space, and continued rapid growth of their role in astronomical research appears certain.

Exploding Galaxies

Perhaps the most important radio astronomy discovery was that certain rare and unusual galaxies emit prodigious quantities of radio energy by some natural process not completely understood. We now have indications that these phenomena, whatever they may be, are connected with enormous explosions occurring near the centers of these systems—explosions that release energy exceeding even that to be expected from nuclear transformations. Once before, astronomers faced a similar problem: what is the source of the energy of the stars? We need only recall the tremendous consequences of the study of that problem, which led to the discovery and understanding of thermonuclear energy sources, to appreciate the import of this greater puzzle.

The discovery of radio explosions in galaxies is one of the most far-reaching of our time because it shows, in addition to the existence of these catastrophic events, that general magnetic fields exist in space between the stars (and perhaps between the galaxies), and that large numbers of high-energy particles of unknown origin are moving through these fields. The discovery undoubtedly provides the long-sought connection between astronomy and cosmic rays. The process that produces the radio emission is called magnetic *bremsstrahlung* or synchrotron radiation. It occurs when high-energy electrons, traveling near the speed of light, encounter a magnetic field. They are deflected by the field in a well-understood way, and in so doing are accelerated, with a subsequent emission of electromagnetic radiation. For certain ranges of electron energies and magnetic-field strengths, this radiation is in the radio region of the spectrum. If the energies and field strengths are high enough, part of the energy can also be radiated in optical wavelengths, and there are well-known examples in which this occurs. The Crab Nebula, which is a remnant of an ancient supernova, is one such example, and the exploding galaxy M82, shown in Figure 1, is another. Direct evidence is available in M82 from optical polarization data to show that magnetic fields exist extending 10,000 light years from the center of the galaxy, and that high-energy electrons interacting with these fields produce the observed radiation. The implication of these data for cosmic-ray astronomy and for the problem of the evolution of galaxies is enormous.

To learn more about these events in space we must have many types of observational data. Information on the amount of radiation in different frequency ranges, i.e., the characteristic continuum spectrum of the sources, must be found. If we know the polarization of the radiation, we can map the pattern of the magnetic fields. The variation of the emitted flux with time gives information on the changing pattern of the fields or on the varying energy distribution of the electrons as the explosion evolves. Parallel studies are needed with large and intermediate-size optical telescopes, to obtain: (1) optical identification of the sources, (2) observations of their optical spectrum to find the radial velocities in the expanding universe and hence their distances, and (3) their apparent luminosities so that the energies involved can be determined.

Quasi-Stellar Radio Sources

Within the past year, the early stages of such a program have brought a discovery of major significance. Parallel optical studies have led to the identification of a few members of an entirely new class of astronomical objects; their presence had been signaled by strong radio emission coming from discrete point sources in the sky. On photographic plates these objects appeared to be like ordinary stars; they have no resolvable disk or extended structure, and are called quasi-stellar sources. The discovery that members of the class have large redshifts showed that we are dealing with very distant objects that are radiating energy at an enormous rate. Calculations made from the combined radio and optical data show that the rate of energy release from these objects is at least 10 times greater than from the brightest normal galaxies known. Indeed, the total energy stored in the exploding system is so high that there is now a considerable question as to the adequacy of thermonuclear energy to account for the phenomenon. Calculations show that the energy stored is equivalent to the explosion of a hydrogen bomb containing one billion solar masses of hydrogen. It appears likely that a new type of energy source is required, and speculation favors a mechanism involving the release of energy stored in the gravitational field of a collapsing body. If a mass equivalent to 100 million suns is compressed into a radius somewhat smaller than the distance from the earth to the sun, enough energy will be released from the gravitational field to account for the quasi-stellar energy sources. Obviously astronomers are only now beginning to assess the implications of this discovery, which may have as great an impact on physical thought as the discovery of nuclear energy or the expansion of the universe. More data of a kind that is difficult to obtain are necessary to explore the possibilities opened up by this discovery. The identification of further sources to the optical limit of our largest telescopes must be achieved; their calculated distances are so much greater than those of previously identified individual objects that cosmological models can be put to an observational test. The spectral-energy distributions, redshifts, polarization, and spatial distribution must be found.

The signals, both in the optical and radio spectral regions, are weak. Unless large radio antenna systems and large optical telescopes had been available, the true nature of these remarkable objects would not have been discovered; further progress in understanding their nature is absolutely dependent upon sufficient access to such facilities. Enough instruments of the necessary size are not now available to support an all-out attack, even on this one major problem, to say nothing of the other pressing problems now awaiting solution.

The quasi-stellar sources are an excellent example of the complementary nature of radio and optical astronomy. New discoveries by radio techniques suggest follow-up studies by optical methods, which may lead in turn to the recognition of previously unsuspected phenomena of great importance.

THE INADEQUACY OF PRESENT FACILITIES

Similar inadequacies of telescopic facilities can be documented in observational astrophysics. Only a few examples need be mentioned. The study of stellar evolution, which leads to a knowledge of the ages of stars and the history of our galaxy, suffers from lack of data at the faintest light levels that can now be reached with only two telescopes in the world, the Lick 120-inch and the Palomar 200-inch telescopes. Studies of galaxies are hampered because too few rotation curves and mass values have been determined, due to the demands of other projects on the few existing large telescopes. Optical measurements of polarization of radio sources cannot be carried on at a rate commensurable with minimum progress in the field.

The recent resurgence of interest in planetary astronomy, encouraged by the space program, has created new demands on existing large telescopes that likewise cannot be met. Commitments to programs already in progress have made it difficult for observatories with large telescopes to divert time to ground-based re-evaluation of many parameters of planets and their atmospheres, which are of vital importance in planning vehicular missions to points in the solar system.

Nearly every phase of observational astrophysics is hampered today because the rate of growth of new astronomical facilities has not kept pace with the increasing demand for fundamental data. In optical astronomy, we are living largely on the legacy of the past, using instruments handed down to us from the era of private financing. In radio astronomy, U. S. instruments are too few in number and not powerful enough to accomplish the tasks demanded of them. If astronomy is to progress, major new facilities are needed.

After considering the present serious situation, this Panel proposes the construction of the new facilities in optical and radio astronomy discussed in detail in Sections III and IV. In broad outline, we propose the construction of three major optical telescopes of the 150- to 200-inch size, four intermediate-size telescopes (60 to 84 inches), a number of smaller instruments capable of important bright-star research and training, two major array-type radio telescopes capable of high resolution, two large parabolic steerable antennas of the 300-foot class, and a number of special-purpose radio instruments for the unique problems of great importance.

THE RELATION OF GROUND-BASED AND SPACE ASTRONOMY

The foregoing recommendations, discussed and documented in Sections III and IV, are for new ground-based installations. What is the relation of these proposed facilities to the great potential of astronomy done from space? The conclusion of the Panel, based on the considerations outlined below, is that the existence of our new space capability increases the need for new ground-based facilities.

The possibility of making observations from space above the influence of the earth's atmosphere is a prospect long dreamed of by astronomers. New regions of the electromagnetic spectrum will be immediately accessible to observation, and the chance of making fundamental discoveries about unknown processes and events in the universe is extremely high. The three principal reasons for going into space are: (1) The atmosphere cuts out almost all radiation with wavelengths shorter than 3000 A, and absorbs many important regions of the optical infrared, as well as the long-wavelength radio spectrum. (2) Turbulence in the atmosphere sets a limit of about one-half arc second to the optical resolution of big telescopes. (3) The background radiation that sets the detection limit with a given telescope can be reduced by going into an orbit above the airglow of the upper atmosphere where the remaining background due to zodiacal light is estimated to be one half to one tenth as bright.

Examples of important problems that can be dealt with only from space are: (1) the detection of gamma- and X-radiation, which give evidence of ultra-high-energy events; (2) the measurement of the intermediate ultraviolet and X-ray spectra of the sun and stars; (3) the study of the absolute intensity of the zodiacal light; (4) the detection of the cosmic light from the unresolved background galaxies; and (5) the bringing back of physical samples of the surface materials of the moon and planets. High-resolution photographs may be obtained from less-expensive balloon-borne telescopes.

It is important to realize, however, that these key data obtained from space vehicles will in many cases need to be supplemented by observations that can be obtained quickly and easily from the ground. Examples would include: (1) optical identification of the objects that emit X-ray and gamma-ray radiation on direct photographs, followed by detailed spectrographic studies; (2) observation of the energy distribution in ordinary optical wavelengths of those stars for which extreme-ultraviolet data have been obtained, particularly those objects that show abnormalities; (3) galaxy counts to the optical limit of the largest telescopes to interpret the space data on the cosmic light; (4) planetary studies suggested by space results, such as temperature mapping and high-resolution spectra for identification of atmospheric gases. If the capability for rapid acquisition of this back-up information does not exist, the space data will not be integrated into as rich or complete a picture as is otherwise possible.

Astronomy from the ground and astronomy from space complement each other. One provides the bulk of the data easily; the other provides certain key data, inaccessible from the earth, with commensurately great effort. Each mode of observation sees a part of the universe in a different way, and therefore each must be exploited.

The cost of launching telescopes will be borne by the space program, and since the cost will exceed, by a large factor, any of the items contained in our recommendations, it is not appropriate to consider here the admittedly huge problem of funding space telescopes. An example of the costs is furnished by the 36-inch telescopes now under construction for the Orbiting Astronomical Observatories. Each instrument will cost $60 million launched, and each is designed to last one year. Comparable numbers for a similar telescope on the ground are $0.3 million for the basic instrument and a lifetime of at least 50 years. Even with a generous allowance for the greater efficiency of space telescopes arising from better resolution and the darker sky background, the cost of doing the same observations from space that could be done from the ground is at least 100 times greater. Obviously, no observation that can be done from the ground should be done with a space telescope. These instruments must be reserved for observations that they alone can make.

A proper balance in expenditures for space equipment and for ground-based instruments must be achieved if astronomical knowledge on all fronts is to be gained at an optimum rate. The Panel's recommendations for new facilities are based both on the genuine needs of ground-based astronomy in its own right and on the equipment needed to adequately supplement the space program. It would indeed be unrealistic to concentrate support on the space effort without corresponding attention to the requirements for terrestrial facilities. More ground-based telescopes are needed if necessary data are to be obtained with sufficient speed at minimum cost.

Our recommendations cover the next 10 or 15 years in ground-based astronomy. They are, in a sense, minimal. That is, for example, we do not recommend construction projects that technically could be carried out, such as a 400-inch optical telescope, though it would be of benefit to the science. We believe that the recommendations are realistic in terms of what can be achieved within our present technology and of what will be of most benefit from 1965 to 1975 and some years beyond in the present wave of advance. If new facilities are not created, either through private funding or through government support, then gifted young astronomers will turn to other fields, the promise of astronomy will remain unfulfilled, and American astronomy will surely stagnate in this century.

II THE PRESENT POSITION IN GROUND-BASED ASTRONOMY

It is clear that ground-based astronomy has spread before it a wealth of inviting prospects. Questions of the most fundamental nature regarding the structure and evolutionary history of the universe can be asked with reasonable hope of obtaining answers. But on one frontier after another the growth of knowledge is limited because we need far more extensive observational data than we now have.

What new facilities are needed to exploit the opportunities? In arriving at a recommended program, the Panel has considered the existing facilities, and has reviewed how they came into being and were brought to their present state of operating efficiency. It has compared the technical capabilities of existing proven telescopes with the requirements set by the observational tasks now clearly foreseen. It has also considered a projection of astronomical manpower over the next ten years, to keep the facilities and the number of observing outlets in step with the demands of a growing body of researchers, and yet not outrun the expected supply of experienced instrumentalists and observers needed to build and operate the new major installations proposed. The Panel presents here its evaluations of the present position as a background for the recommendations that follow in Sections III and IV.

THEORETICAL ASTROPHYSICS

Before extensive new facilities are recommended, it is necessary to inquire whether progress in understanding the universe is not as dependent on interpretation of old observations in the light of known physical laws, and on the new ideas that may thus come from theoretical astrophysicists, as it is on accumulation of still more observations. In the early decades of the 20th century, when the highly successful mountain-top observatories in the western United States were exploring the virgin fields laid open by the great new telescopes, it was perhaps true that not enough time was spent on relating observations to theoretical knowledge. The interpretations were not long in coming, but they came mainly from elsewhere. The foundations of modern theoretical astrophysics—theories of stellar atmospheres, the internal constitution of the stars, and cosmology, for example—were laid in Europe, where cloudy skies and small telescopes discouraged rapid development of observational astronomy.

The Panel believes that any imbalance that may once have existed in this country has long since been corrected. At many universities in the United States there are groups of mature practitioners of theoretical astrophysics. Graduate schools give every young astronomer in training a basic grounding in the subject, and at certain centers a number of students prepare for careers in that field. Physical scientists trained in neighboring fields have become interested in astronomy and have made major theoretical contributions to problems of thermonuclear energy sources, to stellar evolution, and to the radiation physics of radio sources, for example.

Another desirable development has been the near disappearance of the separation between observationalists and theorists. Quite a number of U.S. astronomers are adept in both roles, and a balance in the numbers of specialists of the two types is maintained in most university graduate departments. Through frequent visitation and extended sojourns at major centers, the pure theoretical astrophysicists maintain fairly continuous contact with the latest observational results, and there is immediate feedback of their ideas into proposed new observations.

The Panel concludes that progress in observational astronomy is not idea-limited. The limitation is still well on the side of observations, which come much more slowly than the flashes of insight that may be their initial inspiration.

While the Panel has concentrated its attention on the facilities needed to accelerate the acquisition of new observational data about the universe, it also recognizes the great importance of a continuing buildup of strength on the theoretical side.

OPTICAL ASTRONOMY

Present Dominant Position of the United States

The position of leadership that the United States enjoys in optical astronomy has been won as a direct result of its superior observing facilities. The event of greatest historic significance was the building of the 36-inch refractor at Lick Observatory on Mount Hamilton in the 1880's. This was the first permanently occupied mountain observatory anywhere, and quickly demonstrated the advantages of such a site. The great success of the 36-inch Crossley reflector at Lick Observatory a few years later led naturally to the perfecting of the large modern reflecting telescope, with all its advantages for astrophysical research. The founding of the Mount Wilson Observatory with its 60-inch reflector, completed in 1908, and its 100-inch in 1918, was perhaps the decisive step toward achieving leadership. It was not entirely a matter of size and superior atmospheric conditions, however. The insistence of the builders of all these pioneering telescopes on the highest standards of optical and mechanical performance also contributed to their spectacular success. The McDonald 82-inch telescope in West Texas in 1939, the giant 200-inch reflector on Palomar Mountain in 1949, and the 120-inch reflector at Lick Observatory in 1959 complete the list of the telescopes that have continued the tradition. All save the last were private gifts; the 120-inch was financed by tax monies of the State of California. These great telescopes are the peculiar American contribution to the development of astronomy. Instruments like them are so essential to astronomers that new large telescopes are being planned in other parts of the world. A 104-inch reflector at the Crimean Observatory in the U.S.S.R. is just getting its auxiliary instruments, and a 237-inch for a mountain site in the U.S.S.R. is being planned. A 150-inch reflector for the Southern Hemisphere is being planned by a group of European countries, and another one of similar size for the Southern Hemisphere is being discussed by British Commonwealth nations. The momentum of the American observatories will not be quickly overcome, but inevitable continuation of a position of leadership should not be assumed.

The Limiting Factor for Future Success

With these excellent instruments in the good-climate areas of the western United States, what limits more rapid progress on the unsolved problems already opened up? The Panel believes that it is not a lack of a unifying theoretical concept or of new ideas, as explained earlier; nor is it the lack of a proper number of skilled and imaginative observational astronomers. It is not the need to wait for crucial bits of data from space telescopes, helpful as these may be in certain cases. Neither is it delay in the construction of a larger telescope than any yet made to get past an all-important threshold of information. The limiting factor is, rather, simply *the extremely small number of telescopes of adequate size in dark-sky locations* and the consequent slow accumulation of urgently needed observational data. Only a handful of astronomers can now be engaged in a sustained attack on frontier problems at any one time.

This dilemma arises because astronomical sources are so faint that telescopes of the largest size are required for at least part of most problems. If we compute the output capacity of all telescopes with adequate light-collecting area now in operation anywhere, and compare this with the crucial problems requiring certain numbers of photon-hours for their solution, we immediately perceive that our present instrumental facilities are entirely inadequate to meet the astronomical demand. Thus data precious to the advance of astrophysics are presently denied us.

Only two existing telescopes are adequate for pushing current frontier problems to the observational limit. These are the Lick 120-inch and the Palomar 200-inch reflectors. (The 100-inch telescope on Mount Wilson has lost effectiveness because of the light from nearby metropolitan areas.) These two telescopes do not begin to satisfy the requirements of mid-20th century astronomy. Experience over the past 20 years at the McDonald, Lick, Mount Wilson, and Palomar Observatories, shows that the most efficient exploitation of large telescopes requires carrying on several programs at once—work on faint objects at the photometric limit during the dark of the moon, and spectroscopic work during moonlight. There is, however, an optimum number of perhaps 10 long-term problems that can be handled at any one time—giving each of them about 35 nights a year. Even then, such problems as the distance scale of the universe, where cepheid variables must be found and measured in galaxies, require two to four years to complete at this rate, because of the large number of plates required. This means that 10 to 15 staff astronomers per major telescope is all that can be effective. With only two major frontier telescopes operating, this means that no more than two or three astronomers in the entire world now have the opportunity to work on the most exciting problems in any given field. Competition and the obviously needed opportunity to check results are lacking. The problem, serious enough from the standpoint of progress, is even more serious in another respect: it squeezes out of research life at the frontier top-notch men who, by accident, are not among the fortunate staff members of big observatories. This is an extremely undesirable situation from many points of view.

The problem can be, and is, documented every month by the administrations of both Lick and Mount Wilson-Palomar, where meritorious projects by competent "outside" astronomers must be turned down time after time for lack of guest-investigator time at the telescopes.

The establishment of the Kitt Peak National Observatory will begin to ease the problem, but it is so acute that the establishment of only one more major telescope (the 150-inch) is not a sufficient answer. This is partly because Kitt Peak will be the only non-private instrument available to the *more than 100 observer candidates*. (Neither the Lick nor the Mount Wilson and Palomar Observatories are federally supported institutions, and their instruments are not generally available.) If the yearly assigned observing time on any large telescope is cut below 15 nights per project, no real major problem can be completed successfully in less than three or four years, which is extremely long by modern standards. There will, of course, be a few spectacular one-shot discoveries made with only a few nights, but the follow-up of these leads, so essential in the orderly, progressive advance of astronomy, will be missing.

The inadequacy of the existing large telescopes for the difficult problems involving faint sources would be even more acute if telescopes of lesser size could not be used to carry the considerable fraction of the needed observations that do not demand such great light-gathering power. Telescopes of intermediate size can perform all the standard observational tasks over most of the brightness range covered by objects of a given class. For some types of measurement, such as the study of nebulae, there is almost no loss of efficiency in going to a quite modest telescope.

Recent astronomy is replete with examples of the most productive use of telescopes of small and intermediate size. Examples are: (1) photoelectric photometry of hundreds of star clusters to determine color-magnitude diagrams, (2) the study of the rotation of galaxies from spectrographic radial velocities, (3) spectroscopic studies of physical conditions and abundance ratios in gaseous nebulae, (4) the study of intrinsic variable stars and eclipsing binaries, (5) narrow-band filter photometry for determining luminosity and chemical composition of stars, and (6) objective prism surveys for the discovery of peculiar emission objects and the identification of stars of a particular class.

Interest in these valuable lines of research has maintained a steady pressure on telescopes of small and intermediate size, which has been only partly relieved by the facilities already completed at the Kitt Peak National Observatory. The inadequacy so strongly felt at the largest telescopes is equally critical all along the line, and plans to bolster observing power by building new telescopes must give attention to the whole range of sizes in order to provide an efficient set of observing tools tailored to the varied observational needs of the astronomical community.

RADIO ASTRONOMY

Present Position of the United States

The United States now has an impressive group of major radio telescopes; contrary to the situation in optical astronomy, however, it can not be said that the American position is dominant. The first line of American telescopes, all constructed in the recent past, includes three large telescopes: the 1,000-foot fixed-mirror instrument at Arecibo, Puerto Rico, the 300-foot paraboloid at the National Radio Astronomy Observatory (NRAO), and the 600-foot cylindrical paraboloid of the University of Illinois; the latter two are transit instruments. Then there are the two-element interferometers at the California Institute of Technology and NRAO, and the soon-to-be-completed, 140-foot, fully steerable radio telescope at NRAO. As powerful as these instruments are, they are exceeded in capability (in ways to be discussed later) by such foreign instruments as the 210-foot telescope in Australia, the 22-meter millimeter-wave telescope near Moscow, and the large cross-type arrays nearing completion near Sydney and Moscow. A further development that will outrank American telescopes in capability is the proposed high-resolution instrument to be constructed by the Benelux nations.

Need for High Angular Resolution

Even more important than the capabilities of U. S. radio telescopes relative to those in other parts of the world, however, is the capacity of these telescopes to provide the key data required by the central problems now confronting radio astronomers. In one field of research after another, existing and projected telescopes fall short in one all-important respect: angular resolution. The reason for the exceedingly fuzzy view of the radio sky given by these instruments is that they are not large enough, measured in units of the wavelength of the received radiation, to narrow the instrumental diffraction pattern to effective levels. It must be remembered that radio telescopes differ from optical telescopes in their ability to resolve fine detail because the wavelengths of the radio waves are as much as a million times longer than the wavelength of the optical radiation.

Figure 1   The peculiar galaxy M82 in hydrogen light. The filaments extending upward and downward are composed of material thrown out by an explosion in the nuclear region of the galaxy about 1 million years ago.

Figure 2 The spiral galaxy M31, with its two companions, as photographed with an optical telescope giving a resolution of 1 second of arc.

Figure 3 The galaxy M31 as it would appear to a telescope giving a resolution of 34'.

Figure 4 The galaxy M31 as seen with 12' resolution.

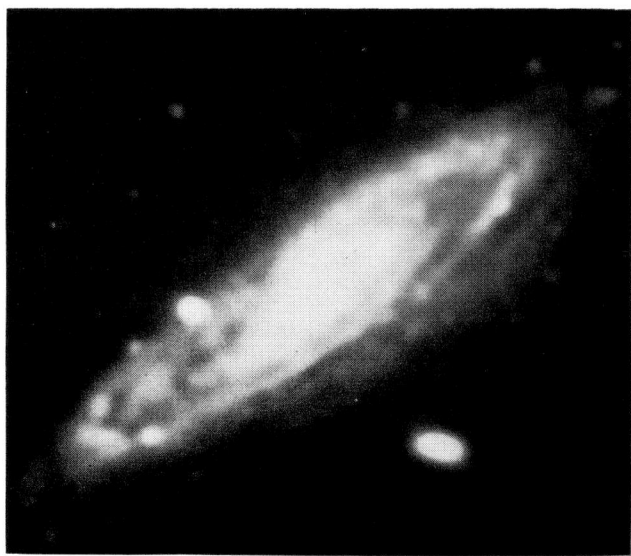

Figure 5 The galaxy M31 as seen with 3' resolution.

Figure 6 The galaxy M31 as seen with 1' resolution.

Figure 7 The spiral galaxy M81 as seen with an optical telescope giving 1" resolution.

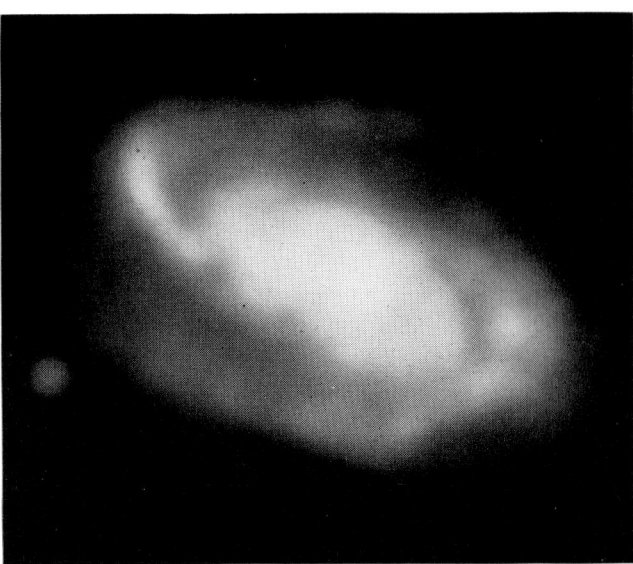

Figure 8 The spiral galaxy M81 as seen with 1' resolution, better than that possible with existing radio telescopes.

Figure 9 The whirlpool galaxy, M51, as seen with an optical telescope giving 1" resolution.

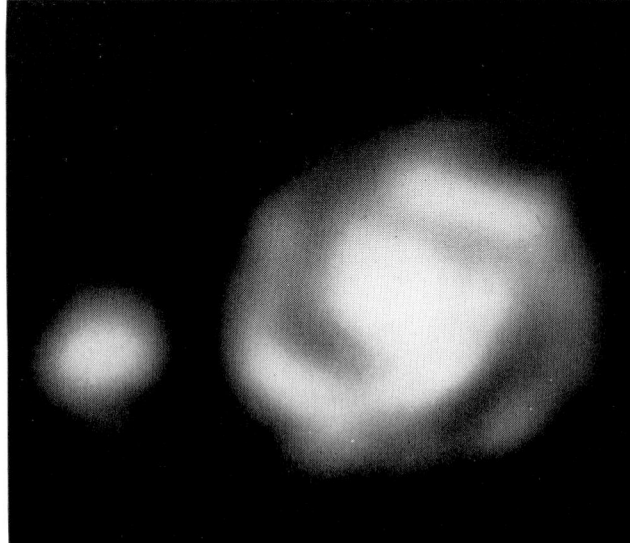

Figure 10 The whirlpool galaxy as seen with 1' resolution.

Figure 11 The barred spiral galaxy NGC 1300, as seen with an optical telescope giving 1" resolution.

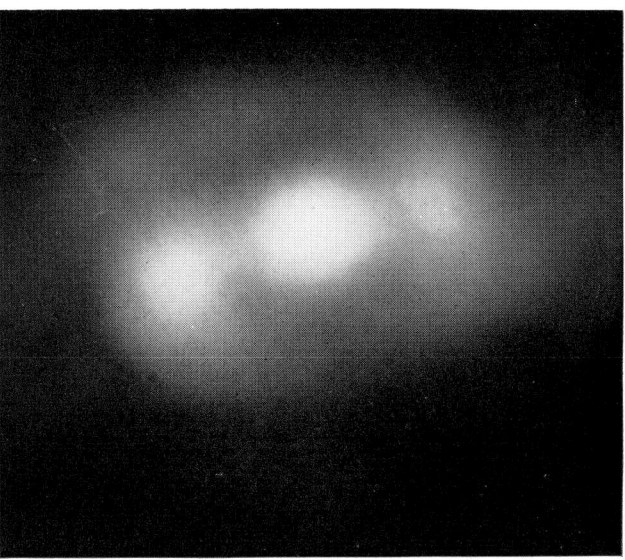

Figure 12 The barred spiral galaxy NGC 1300, as seen with 1' resolution, beyond the capability of existing radio telescopes.

Figure 13 A sample of simulated sky populated with randomly distributed radio sources of a considerable range of intensities, seen under high resolution. The area shown contains about 10 square degrees.

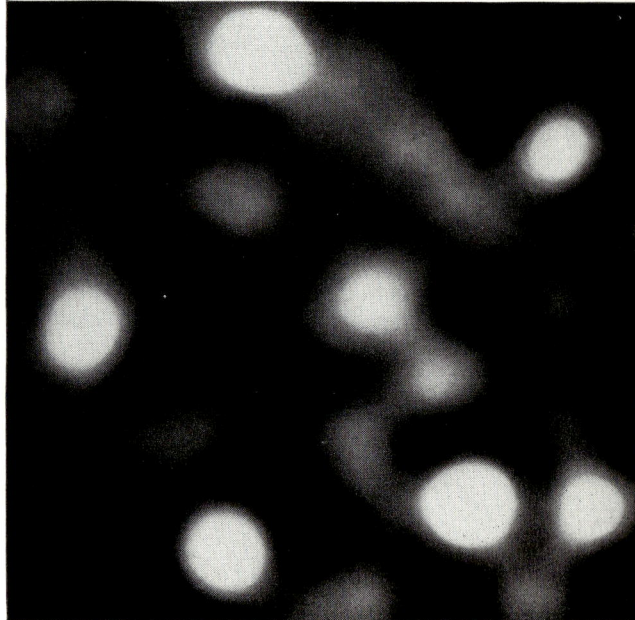

Figure 14 The model sky of Figure 13 as it would be seen at a resolution of 7', or about that possible with a 300-foot radio telescope working at 21 cm.

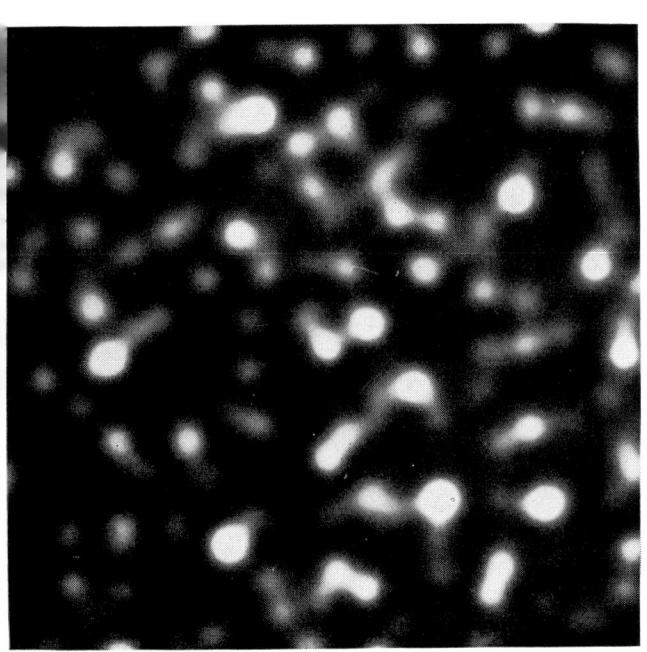
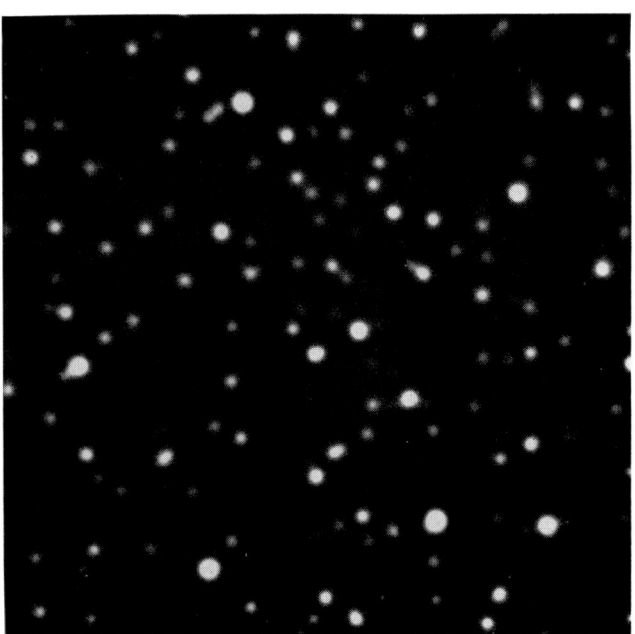

Figure 15 The model sky of Figure 13 at a resolution of 3'.

Figure 16 The model sky of Figure 13 at a resolution of 1', beyond the capability of any existing radio telescopes.

Thus the major factor that limits the advance of radio astronomy today is not particularly lack of observing time with frontier instruments, as in the case of optical astronomy, but rather the lack of instruments of the proper design to meet problems now recognized.

Two important facts should be recognized in an analysis of the American—and the world-wide—program in radio telescopes: 1) None of the proposed or existing instruments will provide the versatility, the speed, and particularly the resolution demanded for substantial progress with the prime astronomical problems. The only instrument that approaches the requirements is the proposed antenna system for the California Institute of Technology; its limitations are that its resolution is not sufficiently good, its energy-collecting area is limited, and its sidelobe levels are high. Thus it may reach only the strongest sources effectively. The resolving power of all the other existing instruments falls far short of the required specifications. 2) Contrary to the situation in optical astronomy, radio telescopes have not yet nearly approached the ultimate limitations in performance produced by inhomogeneities of the earth's atmosphere. Theory and preliminary experiments have indicated that the ultimate atmospheric limitations on radio-telescope resolution will be about the same as those for optical telescopes—a fraction of a second of arc. Thus, there is no natural barrier that prevents building radio telescopes on the ground with an angular resolution far beyond that yet achieved, and thus to go beyond an all-important threshold of information.

Turning now specifically to the problems presented by existing radio resolution, we demonstrate graphically the effects of this resolution through the presentation of actual photographs of celestial objects made with a resolution simulating that of radio telescopes. These photographs were prepared by Dr. J. S. Högbom at Leiden Observatory, using optical plates from the Mount Wilson and Palomar Observatories. In preparing these illustrations, a technique is used in which high-quality optical photographs, which have an effective resolution of a few seconds of arc, are reproduced with an out-of-focus enlarger that simulates accurately the performance of a radio telescope of interest.

Resolution of Radio Galaxies

The loss of detail in viewing a nearby galaxy is shown in a series of pictures made by the above procedure. A standard photograph of the giant spiral galaxy M31 is shown in Figure 2. Its optical image has a major axis of about

180′. In Figure 3 we see the galaxy as it would appear to a telescope with 34′ resolution, a value given by present 85-foot telescopes at 21-cm wavelength. It is obvious that at this resolution all detail disappears, except for the flattening of the galaxy. More alarming, the image of the small elliptical galaxy near M31 merges with the image of M31, giving the illusion that M31 perhaps possesses a jet of radiating material. Such structures actually occur in some very abnormal galaxies, and so it is very undesirable that an effect such as this may appear spuriously. Figure 4 shows the galaxy as seen with 12′ resolution, about the resolution of the 300-foot telescope at 21-cm wavelength. Still most of the important spiral structure of the galaxy is indiscernible, and Doppler studies of the rotation of the hydrogen gas in the spiral arms can give only a blurred picture of the motion. Figure 5 shows the galaxy with 3′ resolution, about that obtainable with the 1,000-foot telescope, were it able to reach the declination of this object. At this resolution, important detail begins to appear in the outer part of the object, but the important nuclear regions remain unresolved. Finally, in Figure 6, where the resolution is 1′, a clear picture of the nuclear structure is beginning to appear, and there is hope that a clear observational picture of the physical structure of this object could be obtained. Yet no existing telescope can achieve this resolution. Equally discouraging is the fact that this is the galaxy of greatest apparent size in the northern sky. To gain a clear understanding of the structure of the various forms of galaxies in the universe, a large number of more-distant objects must be observed, and a resolution of the order of seconds of arc will be required.

Examples of the difficulty in observing more-distant objects are shown in Figures 7-12. Figure 7 is a photograph of the galaxy M81, whose major axis measures about 20′. Figure 8 shows the galaxy as it would appear at the presently unavailable 1′ resolution. Much important detail has been lost. Figure 9 is the famous Whirlpool nebula, about 8′ in diameter, and Figure 10 is its image with a 1′ resolution. Its true form is only barely discernible, and the structure of the nuclear regions is lost. Figure 11 shows the barred spiral galaxy NGC 1300, and Figure 12 its image again with a 1′ resolution. Such a radio picture, standing alone, might well be only a controversial enigma.

Resolution and the Cosmological Problem

The important role of resolution in radio astronomy is nowhere more clearly demonstrated than in radio observations associated with problems of cosmology. It is now well established that moderate-size radio telescopes have sufficient sensitivity to detect numerous radio sources even at the bounds of the observable universe. Thus, in principle, the changes in number, density, brightness, and spectrum of these sources can be examined over the vast eons of time spanned as we look to such great distances. From such studies, the history of the universe can, in principle, be determined. However, this can be accomplished only if we can see the most distant sources clearly, which is to say that the telescope resolution must be sufficient to distinguish well the most distant sources from one another and from nearer sources. It can be calculated that this requires the clear resolution of all radio sources when the total number of sources visible in the whole sky is about one million.

Figure 13 shows a sample of about 10 square degrees of a simulated sky possessing in all about one million sources distributed randomly. Figure 14 shows this model as it appears with a resolution of 7′, a little better than the resolution of the 300-foot telescope working at 21 cm, and the resolution of most existing 85-foot telescopes at their shortest operating wavelengths. It is obvious that none of the fainter sources can be reached at all with such resolution. Figure 15 shows the model as seen with 3′ resolution, about that of the 1,000-foot or 140-foot antennas, each working at the shortest wavelength that its accuracy permits. The picture of the sky obtained is still quite inaccurate. A striking feature here is the high frequency with which apparent double and multiple sources appear spuriously. Double sources appear to be a common feature of the real radio sky, so a spurious production of them is an extremely serious defect in any observing instrument. Lastly, Figure 16 is a view of the model with 1′ resolution, presently not available. Only at this resolution is a clear rendition of the model beginning to appear. However, close comparison between Figures 13 and 16 shows that further resolution will be required if a truly accurate reproduction of the model is to be obtained. In actual fact, it can be calculated that a resolution of 30″ or better is required to produce a picture adequate for cosmological computations. Clearly, from the preceding figures, no definitive knowledge of the radio sources throughout the universe can be obtained until resolution of the order of seconds of arc is available to radio astronomers.

Methods of Achieving High Angular Resolution

Increased resolution can be obtained only by increasing the linear size of the antenna system. Fortunately, it is unnecessary to build a single antenna that fills the complete area spanned by the most distant components of the system. Separate, relatively small antennas spaced on a long baseline give the necessary pattern of high resolution with a small total area.

A prime example of this approach is the Mills cross in Australia, in which a large number of simple dipole energy collectors are spaced out on the ground in the pattern of a cross; in the similar Christiansen cross, small paraboloids receive the energy. The widely spread energy collectors are connected electrically so that the performance imitates well the performance of a complete reflector of as great dimension as the largest dimension of the cross pattern.

Another advance is the development in England of a scheme for using two-element interferometer antennas on a variable baseline in such a manner that, after many observations at different times, the electrical performance of a completely filled aperture of great dimension can be imitated, or "synthesized." These interferometer experiments have brought great attention to the concept that any distribution of radio sources, or radio "brightness" in the sky, can be represented as an infinite Fourier series of intensities of all spatial wavelengths projected on the sky. An interferometer, at any instant, is recording one of these Fourier components. Given time, enough components can be obtained to allow a combination in a Fourier synthesis that reproduces with good accuracy the appearance of the radio sky. It now appears that, if sufficient care is taken with the observations, this technique can produce accurate high-resolution radio maps of the sky. The procedure is being pursued with vigor in England and at other places. It becomes evident from any careful study of the aperture-synthesis technique, however, that the procedure is a very lengthy and tedious one; furthermore, when a large number of Fourier components are needed, as is the case where extreme resolution is required, it becomes very difficult to maintain sufficient accuracy in the measurement of the phases and amplitudes of the Fourier components.

A compromise solution to the problem is to use many receiving elements simultaneously, so that many Fourier components are received simultaneously. A judicious choice can be made of the Fourier components to be received, so that the prime astrophysical information about the source in question is emphasized. The result is a rapid acquisition of data, and a system in which errors in phase and amplitude are more easily discovered and corrected, leading to acceptable accuracy in the results. The Mills and Christiansen crosses are, in fact, examples of this procedure. It has become clear that, if the required resolutions of a few seconds of arc are to be obtained with the financial and technological resources realistically presumed to be available, this indirect but effective procedure must be used.

Rapid steps in this direction are being taken. Examples are the construction of the 1.6-km cross of the University of Sydney, now nearing completion; the 1-km cross nearly completed by the Lebedev Physical Institute, Moscow; the 1-km cross of the University of Bologna; and the new aperture-synthesis interferometer of Cambridge University. Extensive experience in aperture-synthesis techniques exists in the United States; one of the outstanding interferometers is that of the California Institute of Technology, which has given many young astronomers backgrounds in these techniques. Soon the long-baseline interferometer of the National Radio Astronomy Observatory will have given a new group of scientists experience in this field.

Collecting Area and Sidelobes as Limiting Factors

Two major factors besides resolution must be considered in evaluating radio telescope design: energy-collecting area, and secondary responses or sidelobes off the main beam. The two are interconnected.

Secondary responses or sidelobes arise from the fact that every antenna collects a small amount of energy from all parts of the sky. In certain directions, this response may be an appreciable fraction of the response in the main beam, i.e., from the direction the telescope is pointing. When the sidelobe response from a strong source equals or overwhelms that from weak sources in the main beam, confusion and error result, since the receiver sums all the received energy. This problem is particularly acute when only two or very few antenna elements occupy the space between the extreme separation required for specified resolution; hence the need to reduce the so-called grating response by adding the many Fourier components previously mentioned.

One solution is to fill in the area between the two extremities completely. This is done in the paraboloid, for which the sidelobe trouble is negligible. The collecting area is enormously increased and signals from weak sources are lifted out of the background noise present in all radio receivers. The advantages of paraboloids for many problems, discussed in a later paragraph, are well known. But in achieving resolution the area is wastefully used, since the resolving power goes only linearly with the aperture and the cost goes as the 2.5 power of the aperture. (See Section VI and the Appendix.) As the size increases, the engineering difficulties of holding a precise parabolic shape in a moving system impose severe obstacles. The compromise of a transit instrument, in which the paraboloid moves only about a single east-west axis, reduces these problems somewhat, but limits the observations of a given object to a few minutes each day while it is passing through the north-south plane. A fixed-mirror system permits a still larger aperture at the price of restricted sky coverage.

For mapping and investigations of individual faint radio sources scattered over the sky, it is much more efficient to use multi-element arrays arranged in the form of a cross. There must be a carefully calculated balance between the energy-collecting area needed for a satisfactory signal-to-noise ratio on the weakest sources that are clearly resolved, and the number and spacing of elements required to suppress sidelobes adequately. Too large a "fill-in factor" not only is wasteful, but also, in the case of the paraboloid, it actually brings so many extremely faint sources above the detection level that a larger aperture increases the confusion between such sources by a factor greater than the capacity of the aperture to resolve them. The result is a "confusion-limited," rather than an "intensity-limited," system. On the other hand, too small a "fill-in factor" means higher sidelobes and a limitation to brighter sources.

The means of achieving balance between the three interconnected factors of resolution, energy-collecting area, and suppression of sidelobes are now well understood and are being taken into account in designs for radio telescopes now projected. Techniques have been developed for identifying and eliminating sidelobe responses, with less filling-in of the total aperture-spread of the antenna system than straightforward optical theory would require. By slightly varying the frequency, or by combining the signals from the various collecting elements with an altered set of weighting factors, the sidelobe response can be changed without affecting the main beam appreciably, thus providing a means of separating spurious sources.

Parabolic Antennas

Critical as is the need for high resolution, complex arrays are not the complete answer. A balanced and fully effective program of radio telescopes will include fully steerable single paraboloids of the largest feasible aperture. There is a class of problems, as in the study of variable radio sources, galactic structure, and the polarization of radiation, that do not require the highest resolution. Studies of the 21-cm line of hydrogen and other spectral lines, or any problems that require frequency scanning, are extremely difficult with arrays. Not only for these problems, but also in situations where a telescope is required to serve a heterogeneous group of observers, as at the National Radio Astronomy Observatory, a single paraboloid has been found to be the best solution. Indeed, such an instrument can be operated on widely different frequencies simultaneously, thus facilitating use of different programs on the same day without change of instrumentation. When necessary, instrumentation at the single receiving point can be quickly changed and experimental equipment for exploratory measurement conveniently and cheaply attached. And, not the least in importance, ease of use and versatility make the paraboloid ideal for graduate students, thus giving them personal first-hand experience.

From the foregoing discussion it is clear that straightforward applications of known technology could produce radio telescopes considerably superior to any now existing in the United States. The giant 1,000-foot telescope at Arecibo, Puerto Rico, may produce a resolution of a few minutes of arc, but has limited sky and frequency coverage, and a major part of its observing time is committed to a program of geophysical studies. The 600-foot telescope of the University of Illinois is limited by its frequency coverage to resolutions of the order of 10' of arc, and as a transit instrument it cannot track objects across the sky. The National Radio Astronomy Observatory (NRAO) 300-foot radio telescope is also limited in its frequency and sky coverage, and by its inability to track. The interferometers at the California Institute of Technology and at NRAO (consisting of two 90-foot and two 85-foot antennas respectively) are limited by their small effective collecting area, which restricts them to study of strong sources, and by the speed with which they can acquire data. The compound interferometer at Stanford University, which forms a fan beam less than one minute of arc wide, is limited to less than a dozen sources. Soon the NRAO 140-foot telescope will be finished; it will achieve resolutions of the order of a few minutes of arc at best. There also exist in the United States more than a half-dozen 85-foot-class paraboloids at various institutions. Although these serve well for certain classes of problems, they are too small to provide adequate resolving power and collecting area.

In summary, then, the tremendous U. S. progress in recent years has produced a series of impressive instruments for radio astronomy. Their use has clearly indicated fairly direct paths to profoundly important information about the universe. But none of the instruments now in existence anywhere or authorized for construction are adequate for meeting these challenges. The United States should proceed with production of instruments that will cross the resolution threshold, lest we neglect one of the most significant scientific heritages of our times. The proposals in Section IV look toward a construction program sufficient to overcome the inadequacies we have discussed here.

THE DILEMMA OF THE ASTRONOMY GRADUATE SCHOOL IN 1964

Equally as serious as the problems arising from the lack of large frontier telescopes is the current situation concerning the instrumentation at graduate schools throughout the country. The demand for graduate astronomers is very high. Whereas 15 years ago the few new astronomers produced each year were sufficient to satisfy the immediate needs of that era, today there are not enough astronomers either to satisfy the demands of the space program or to keep pace with expanding university requirements. On the surface, present demand and potential supply might appear to be on the way toward a satisfactory balance. Graduate schools are now flooded with applications in astronomy; enrollment is higher than it ever has been and is increasing at the unprecedented growth rate of 19 per cent a year. (See the discussion of manpower, pp. 28-37.) But herein lies the problem: Of the 30 Ph.D.-granting institutions, only a handful—perhaps three or four—are well enough equipped with adequate instruments to teach astronomy and astrophysics in the manner required. Most departments possess equipment (small telescopes, light detectors, spectrographs, data-reduction instruments) that dates from approximately 40 years ago. These departments are now asked to train students in this modern era. A parallel task would be to maintain high-level research and teaching departments of physics without nuclear accelerators or modern low-temperature laboratories; or to teach chemistry with only Bunsen burners and test tubes; or to teach molecular biology without electron microscopes and X-ray apparatus.

The circumstances leading to the present lack of university research facilities in astronomy can easily be traced. Before World War II, astronomy was an "ivory tower" subject in the university curriculum. Most astronomy departments were small, consisting of one or perhaps two men with very few students. Almost no university could justify the creation of research facilities for such a small fraction of its activity. There were a few institutions, however, that did obtain research equipment, either by gifts from interested outside individuals or from enlightened administrations that strongly supported small but active astronomy programs. These few schools then developed into the only graduate departments in the United States that stressed observational astrophysics, and they are the schools from which most graduate astronomers have emerged. Not only these schools, but also schools that want to *start* astronomy programs, face almost insurmountable problems in the present era with its increased pressure for excellence. Except for a handful of radio telescopes, there have been very few major additions to the equipment of the existing graduate schools for many years. Even more serious is the fact that most of the newly created graduate departments have virtually no instrumental legacy from the past.

This problem was recognized about ten years ago when the discussions leading to setting up the Kitt Peak National Observatory and the National Radio Astronomy Observatory were begun. If the Kitt Peak Observatory did not exist, the situation in optical astronomy would now be almost intolerable. At present, some of the graduate-student pressure is relieved because students from any institution in the country can use the national facility at Kitt Peak. But it is estimated that Kitt Peak can satisfy only 25 per cent of the total demand that will develop in the near future.

Furthermore, there is a fundamental disadvantage in relying solely on the national facilities. Faculty members and students must travel from their home institutions to distant places in order to collect material for their research problems. They then return to their own graduate departments to analyze the data. It is usually the case in all experimental science that, as insight into a problem develops, different data are required or new techniques must be employed at intermediate stages in the research. It is difficult to meet this requirement unless the research facilities are constantly at hand at the home institution. The most efficient use of the telescopes at Kitt Peak and NRAO would be in the final push toward solution of problems, after observational techniques had been thoroughly tested on nearby modern instruments. Thus, the necessarily limited period with a larger telescope and good skies for optical observers could be used far more productively.

It is the opinion of this Panel that a number of graduate schools in the country should be supported in their attempt to acquire moderate-size telescopes so that such a scheme of operation could be adopted generally. There is, of course, a limit to the size of the optical telescope that can be justified in parts of the country with low percentages of clear nights. In the opinion of the Panel, telescopes larger than 48 inches should not be built in areas of relatively poor weather. However, it is abundantly clear from results obtained, for example, at the Case Institute of Technology, the University of

Wisconsin, and the University of Michigan that telescopes of 24- to 40-inch size can and have contributed enormously to the progress of observational astronomy. The research of both faculty and students at these institutions is of high caliber, and exemplifies what can be done under relatively poor sky conditions.

The existence of modern telescopes at individual graduate schools has many advantages. A healthy research atmosphere is almost automatically created among faculty and students alike. The equipment is available for many astronomical problems that could not be solved on an expeditionary basis at a national facility. Special work on novae, comets, planets, and the moon at certain unpredictable times requires observations that could not be made at a national observatory hundreds or even thousands of miles away. Any problem requiring close surveillance, such as those posed by irregular variable stars, eclipsing binaries, intrinsic variables, and the radio emission of Jupiter, cannot be dealt with away from home because the need is for repeated observations at selected times. Most important is the fact that most university-connected astronomers are engaged in teaching and hence are on the campus for three quarters of the year. And this is where the students are. If maximum use is to be made of equipment, it must not be located hundreds of miles away, but must be easily accessible, not more than one hour's travel time away.

MANPOWER

We have now outlined the present position of optical and radio astronomy with respect to the facilities needed for an aggressive attack on problems awaiting solution. There remains the important question of the balance between the creation of facilities and the number of astronomers that will be demanding observing time when the facilities are completed.

The answer to this question cannot be given in hard bookkeeping terms, because the availability of facilities affects the choice that young scientists make on whether to go into theoretical or into observational astronomy. The evidence we have cited earlier in this discussion—the unsatisfied demand for the telescope time at major observing centers and the desire of many university graduate departments for modern, locally based observing equipment—points to the current severe limitations in facilities. Fine new instruments undoubtedly do attract and inspire imaginative use by outstanding young scientists. Without allowance for such intangibles, the Panel has examined the growth rate in the number of astronomers in recent years, and has attempted to set upper and lower limits on the number of U. S. astronomers a decade hence. The conclusion points to no less than a doubling in the next ten years. If the current rapid growth in graduate enrollment continues, the factor of increase may be as large as 2.4.

Training of Astronomers Compared to Training of Other Physical Scientists

Astronomy is one of the smallest disciplines among the engineering, mathematical, and physical sciences. The annual production of Ph.D.'s has been widely used as an index of the growth rate in these fields. The following studies contain material relevant to the present discussion:

Doctorate Production in United States Universities. Office of Scientific Personnel of the National Academy of Sciences—National Research Council, Publication 1142. (See also *Physics Today*, 15:21, 1962 for data on physics Ph.D.'s.)

Comparison of Earned Degrees Awarded 1901-1962 with Projections to 2000. National Science Foundation Report NSF 64-2.

Investing in Scientific Progress. National Science Foundation Report NSF 61-27; also Report NSF 62-43.

Meeting Manpower Needs in Science and Technology. Report No. 1, Graduate Training in Engineering, Mathematical, and Physical Sciences, by President's Science Advisory Committee, Dec. 12, 1962.

The semi-logarithmic plot of Figure 17 shows the annual U. S. Ph.D. production in astronomy, physics, and all physical sciences (first two references above). It is apparent that *over the long term* the country's astronomy education system has not consistently maintained the smoothed growth rate of about 7 per cent per year (doubling time, 10.2 years) that has prevailed in related sciences. The decline in the period 1935-41 may have been caused by the paucity of jobs in astronomy at a time when the field offered many fewer industrial and government openings than were available to physicists.

The Ph.D.-production rate is perhaps a less reliable basis for estimating the U. S. working force in astronomy than in other physical sciences because of the important fraction of foreign-born, foreign-trained scientists in the group. Moreover, there is good evidence that an appreciable proportion of the present astronomy force transferred into astronomy after Ph.D. training in other disciplines, such as physics and engineering. Yet Figure 17 shows

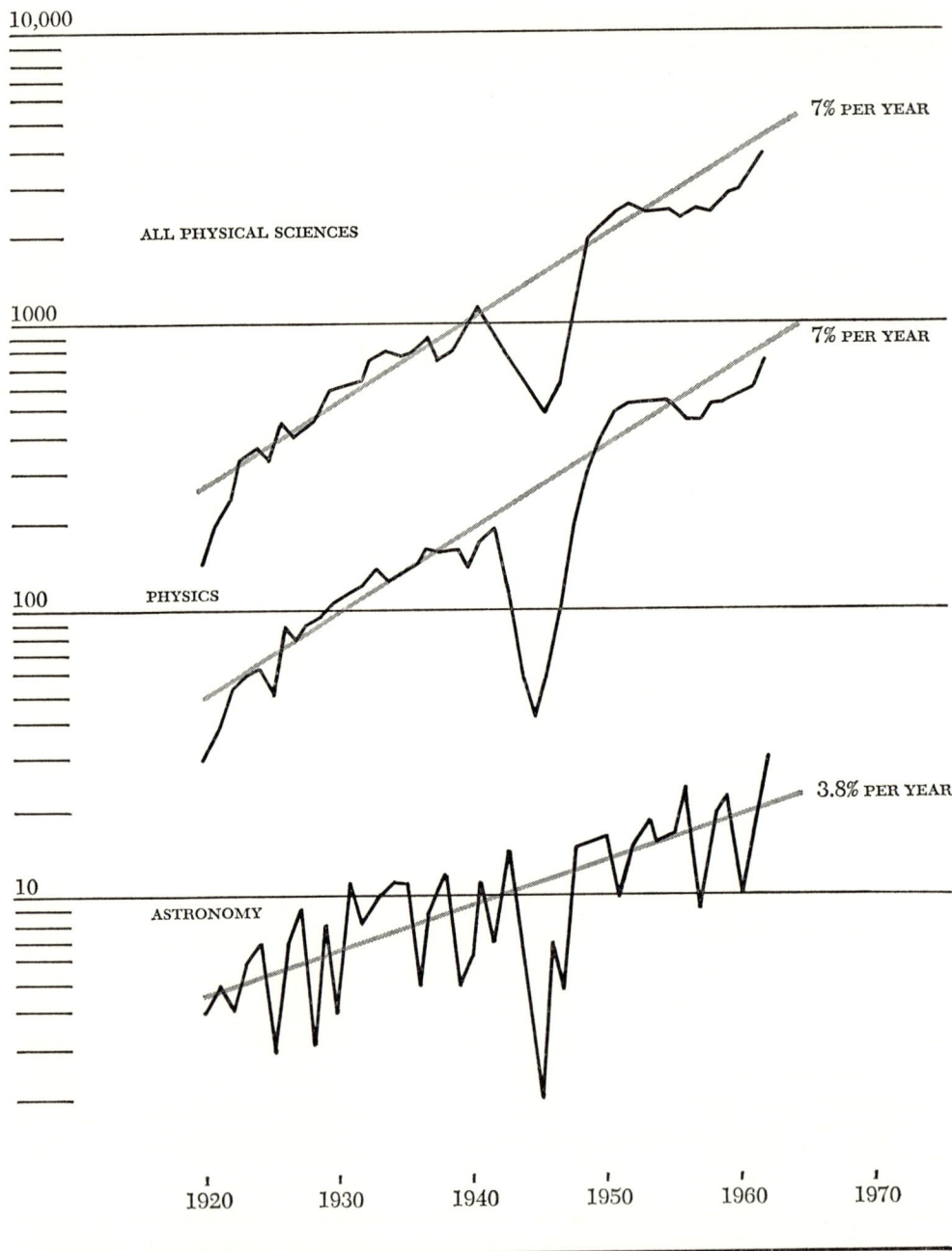

Figure 17
Annual Ph.D. production in astronomy and other physical sciences in the United States.

steady growth at about 3.8 per cent a year (19-year doubling time) through all the postwar years, including the 1950's, when physics-Ph.D. production was on a plateau. Since 1956, there have been signs of an upsurge that may lead to a much higher growth rate. Before exploring the implications and making a projection based on the best current data, it is of interest to consider another index of research activity in astronomy to see if corroborative evidence exists.

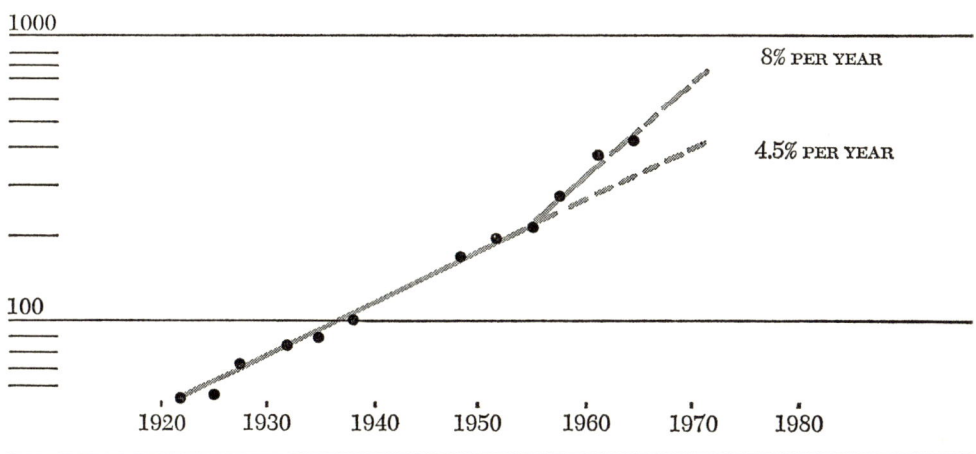

Figure 18
Growth of U.S. membership in the International Astronomical Union 1921-1963, projected to 1972.

U. S. Membership in the International Astronomical Union

Figure 18 shows the number of U. S. members in the International Astronomical Union (IAU) from 1923 to 1961. Membership in the IAU is universal enough among established professional astronomers so that weighting in favor of the international-minded is negligible. Yet the standards of membership are such that, at any one time, a number of young and productive researchers who make heavy demands on facilities are not being counted. The membership figure is therefore lower than the actual force, presumably by a constant percentage in a period of stable growth. The enumeration is insensitive to foreign birth and training, and to transfer into astronomy from initial training in another field.

The plot in Figure 18 shows a steady growth rate of 4.5 per cent per year (doubling time, 16 years) from 1923 to 1955. The three points from 1958 to 1964 show a sharp upturn to a doubling time of nine years. (The 1964 point is an estimate from the U. S. National Committee of the IAU, based on nominations.) This confirms the impression gained from the growth in membership of the American Astronomical Society, and from the rapid swelling of the astronomy graduate student population. Since the latter gives the most up-to-date information, it has been made the subject of a special study.

Graduate Student Population in Astronomy Departments

The current survey grew out of a census made by W. E. Howard III for the 1962 Conference on Graduate Education in Astronomy, held at Bloomington, Indiana. Material for this study was gathered by inquiries to the 28 departments listed in the brochure entitled "Careers in Astronomy," published in 1962 by the Committee on Education in Astronomy of the American Astronomical Society, plus four new departments known to the committee. The replies on the numbers of students in the falls of 1957, 1960, and 1963, plus each department's estimate of the 1966 enrollment, are listed in Table 1. The totals, plotted in Figure 19, establish a growth rate within the graduate schools of 19 per cent a year (a doubling time of 4.0 years). This is nearly twice the rate attained or projected in related sciences. A simple extrapolation predicts 2,590 graduate students in astronomy in 1973. The first effect of this surge was a Ph.D. output of 30 in 1962, considerably higher than in any previous year, but a figure consistent with the assumption that the Ph.D.'s should be at least 10 per cent of the student population, with a three-year lag to allow for the fact that rapid growth means a higher proportion of beginning graduate students.

What is the source of this boom and how long will it continue? In the opinion of the Panel, some of it was a natural growth, stimulated by general awareness among science-inclined undergraduates of the exciting developments in astronomy of the postwar years, and fostered by wise supplementary support of research and instrumentation in many universities by federal agencies. A new and strong influence came with the first Sputnik in 1957 and the widespread interest in space that followed. Since a good part of the university-based space effort is in special institutes separate from astronomy departments—often dominated by physicists, geophysicists, and engineers—the rapidly growing student population in the departmental tabulation of Table 1 represents a broad spectrum of interests, and something like the traditional proportion of the students may be expected to go into ground-based observational astronomy.

The new astronomy students undoubtedly represent a shift in interest

TABLE 1 THE NUMBER OF GRADUATE STUDENTS IN ASTRONOMY BY INSTITUTION

	1957	1960	1963	1966 (EXPECTED)
University of Arizona	0	2	28	35
California Institute of Technology	16	22	19	35
University of California, Berkeley	20	23	35	65
University of California, Los Angeles	3	20	28	40
Case Institute of Technology	1	5	17	20
University of Chicago	6	7	14	20
University of Cincinnati	0	6	4	1
University of Colorado	7	15	42	50
Columbia University	5	5	4	12
Cornell University	2	3	5	7
University of Florida	0	0	12	20
Georgetown University	22	31	40	45
Harvard University	24	28	40	55
University of Illinois	2	8	13	17
Indiana University	15	23	25	30
State University of Iowa	0	0	6	10
Louisiana State University	0	0	2	6
University of Maryland	0	2	25	55
University of Michigan	16	28	32	40
Northwestern University	1	0	11	15
Ohio State University	5	7	14	25
University of Pennsylvania	3	8	15	20
Princeton University	6	6	7	10
Rensselaer Polytechnic Institute	0	1	8	13
University of Rochester	1	2	2	8
Stanford University	5	5	7	12
University of Texas	0	5	12	25
Vanderbilt University	0	0	2	6
University of Virginia	1	0	2	16
Wesleyan University	0	2	6	10
University of Wisconsin	2	14	19	30
Yale University	5	6	28	40
Totals	168	284	524	793

within the 25 per cent fraction of the physical-science doctorates that have been going into astronomy, physics, and geo-sciences (*Doctorate Production in United States Universities,* see p. 30). This percentage has remained stable over many years, as has the over-all fraction of about one sixth of total doctorate production going into all the physical sciences. The shift did not need to be a large one to produce the drastic increase in astronomy alone, since astronomy Ph.D.'s in the years 1957-62 were only 3 per cent of those in physics, rising to just over 4 per cent in 1962. An increase of the astronomy Ph.D.'s to 8 per cent of the physics production, as was the case in the prenuclear decade of the 1920's, or even to 10 or 12 per cent, would not be

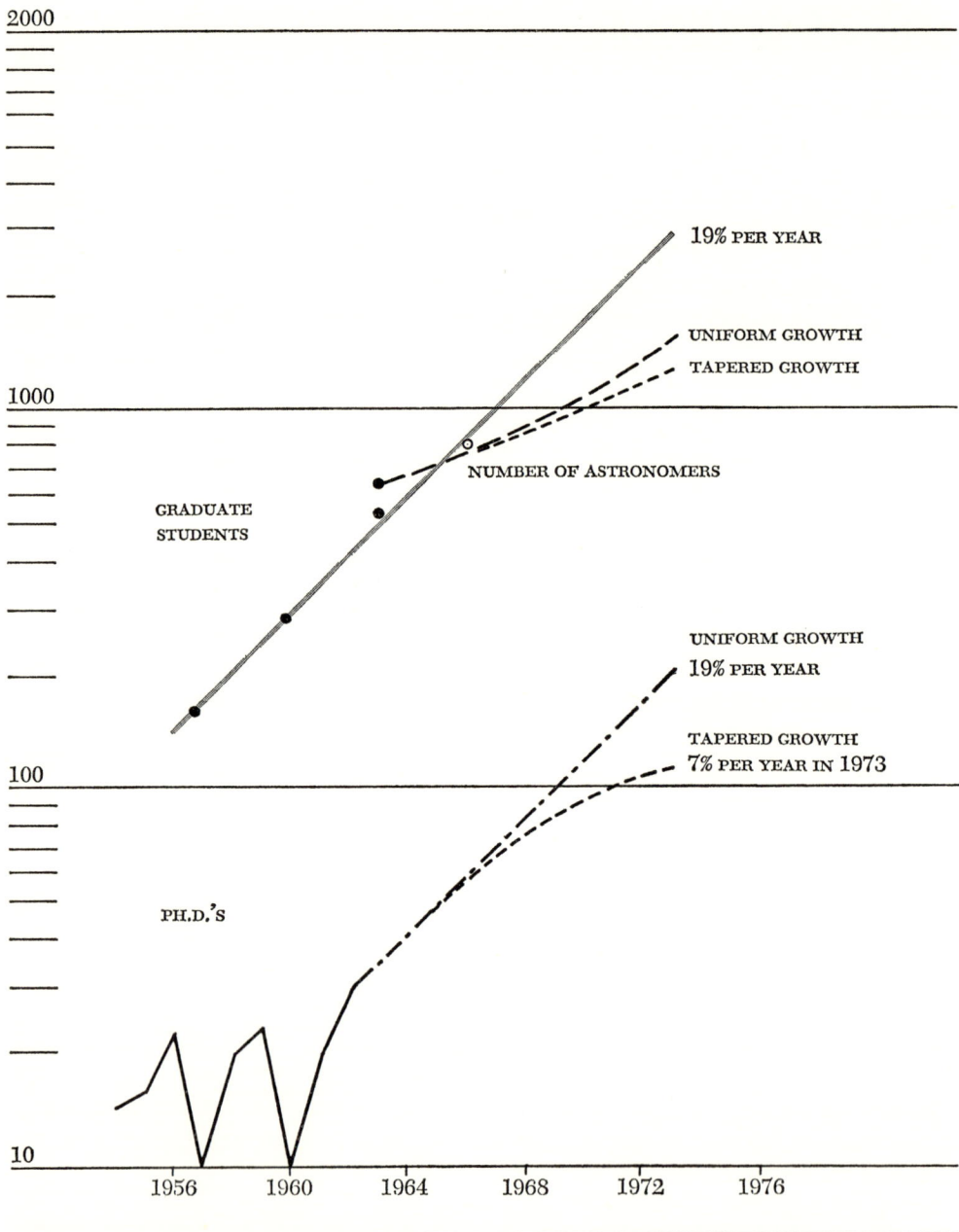

Figure 19
Number of graduate students in astronomy, the number of Ph.D.'s 1954-1962, and projected Ph.D. production and total number of astronomers to 1973.

tantamount to a drastic redistribution of emphasis among the physical sciences, since the number of astronomers is still disproportionately small when compared to the total manpower in physics, geophysics, and astronomy combined.

In order to sustain a high growth rate there must be support for increasing numbers of graduate students. The National Defense Education Act is assisting the graduate population in all the physical sciences, and the effect of the act has not yet reached its maximum point. The new National Aeronautics and Space Administration (NASA) fellowship program supported 100 graduate students in all fields in 10 institutions in 1962-63, and 886 fellows in 1963-64; it is expected to increase, according to NASA sources, to support as many as 4,000 graduate students. In view of the announced purposes of the program, a certain fraction of the recipients could be assumed to be astronomy students who would otherwise have gone into some other physical science. Although it is conceivable that this influence could accelerate the growth rate even beyond the present very high figure, it is probably not safe to attempt such a projection now. The NASA fellowships may be counted, however, as one of the sources of support that will sustain the current rapid expansion of interest in astronomy in the universities.

A Ten-Year Projection

Two projections of the number of astronomers in the United States will be attempted. It may be assumed that the 19 per cent a year growth rate in astronomy graduate-student population has been in effect long enough to achieve a new equilibrium, and that, as long as the growth rate is sustained, the Ph.D. production will also increase at a 19 per cent a year rate, starting from an output of 30 in 1962. For a high estimate of the production, it may further be assumed that the current growth rate in Ph.D. production will remain unchanged in the ten-year period 1963-1973. Since it is difficult to maintain that such a phenomenally high rate can be sustained over a long period, a more conservative estimate must be based on some assumption as to the timing of a tapering off of the growth rate. For the low estimate, a 19 per cent growth rate is assumed for the first year, decreasing uniformly by 1.2 per cent per year to reach the 7 per cent long-term growth rate characteristic of the physical sciences in general by the end of the ten-year period.

Of the 1,360 members of the American Astronomical Society on January 1, 1964, 620 have U. S. addresses and hold doctorates or professorships. This number undoubtedly includes some fringe astronomers and persons

TABLE 2 PREDICTED ASTRONOMICAL MANPOWER IN THE UNITED STATES

UNIFORM GROWTH RATE (19% a year, or 4-year doubling period)

	1963	1964	1965	1966	1967	1968	1969	1970	1971	1972	1973
New Ph.D.'s		43	50	59	71	83	98	118	138	162	195
Sub-total		663	703	751	811	882	967	1071	1193	1337	1512
1.5% Loss		10	11	11	12	13	14	16	18	20	23
Total	620	653	692	740	799	869	953	1055	1175	1317	1489

TAPERED GROWTH RATE (19% a year in first year, decreasing to 7% a year at end)

	1963	1964	1965	1966	1967	1968	1969	1970	1971	1972	1973
New Ph.D.'s		42	49	56	64	72	81	90	98	106	113
Sub-total		662	701	747	800	860	928	1004	1087	1177	1272
1.5% Loss		10	10	11	12	13	14	15	16	18	19
Total	620	652	691	736	788	847	914	989	1071	1159	1253

with primary interests in other fields, but there is probably approximate compensation by the active astronomers in the other 54 per cent of the membership who do not hold doctorates or professorships. The National Register of Scientific and Technical Personnel lists 483 full-time astronomers in the United States in 1962. (W. L. Koltun of the National Science Foundation, which maintains the Register, estimates that the listing, based on responses to a questionnaire, is only 80 per cent complete.) If allowance is made for incompleteness and for about 40 Ph.D.'s added since 1962, and also for the standard loss of 1.5 per cent a year by death or retirement, found by the National Science Foundation to apply generally in scientific-manpower surveys, the corrected total becomes 626 full-time astronomers at the beginning of 1964. This is a confirmation of the previous figure of 620, and that number may be adopted as a base for the projection.

Two projections are worked out in Table 2 and plotted in Figure 19. The high estimate shows an increase in total astronomical manpower by a factor of 2.4 in ten years. The low estimate projects an increase by a factor of 2.0. This tabulation does not attempt to classify astronomers by categories of interest—theoretical or observational, optical or radio, ground-based or space-oriented. Since shifts in emphasis occur quite slowly, no complete overturn in percentages would be expected in a decade. A prediction would be hazardous, but the proportion of the student population in graduate departments that place emphasis on ground-based astronomy, compared with

Special-Purpose Telescopes

Special-purpose wide-field telescopes will not, the Panel believes, become an appreciable fraction of those built in the next few years. The 48-inch Palomar Schmidt telescope has been a superb survey instrument. Experience since the completion of the Palomar Sky Survey has shown that this one instrument can serve the needs of U. S. astronomers for the parts of the heavens accessible to it. A similar instrument is urgently needed in the Southern Hemisphere. It could be identical, or it might be modified to give a larger plate scale at a price of reduced angular field and speed. For surveys to a brighter magnitude limit, the smaller Schmidt telescopes (up to 24-inch aperture) such as those at Michigan and Case, should suffice for the next ten years. Wide-field astrometric refractors, such as the twin Carnegie instrument at Lick Observatory and its counterpart being built for the Yale-Columbia station in Argentina, will not need to be duplicated, since the "ripening time" of proper motion plates is so much longer than the exposure cycle for one complete coverage of the sky and the subsequent evaluation period.

The 60-inch astrometric reflector now being tested at the Flagstaff station of the U. S. Naval Observatory is another special-purpose telescope that should satisfy U. S. demands in its particular field for the next decade.

Solar Telescopes

The completion of the McMath solar telescope at the Kitt Peak National Observatory has given the solar astronomers of the country the largest such telescope in the world. The large aperture (60-inch) gives a bright image, and the careful thermal control of every part of the surroundings gives an opportunity for high-resolution spectroscopy of fine details of the solar surface. Still another facility at the Air Force-Sacramento Peak Observatory is in the late planning stages, and construction seems assured. The loss of resolution caused by turbulent air currents within the optical system (internal seeing) is to be solved by placing the entire telescope and spectrograph in a vacuum. In view of these major additions to facilities, the Panel feels that it would be wise to await evaluation of the new instrumental techniques being employed before recommending construction of further solar telescopes. The Panel believes, however, that solar researchers should be vigorously supported in the development of new auxiliary instruments and in the testing of new methods.

SIZE CATEGORIES

The optical telescopes that could be built in the next ten years may be divided into the following arbitrary size categories:

> Giant: diameter larger than 250 inches
> Large: 100-200 inches
> Intermediate: 60-84 inches
> Small: 36-48 inches

Except for the giant class, the size ranges listed are those represented by existing U. S. telescopes. The gaps are not significant, except in the sense that a ready-made, highly successful design cannot be taken over for the in-between sizes without some scaling up or down.

PERFORMANCE VERSUS SIZE

The Panel's decision on what telescopes to recommend for funding has required balancing scientific objectives against size, cost, and time for construction. A brief résumé of the interdependence of these factors is necessary to make clear the decisions finally taken.

Faint star images must be detected against the unavoidable background of the light of the night sky. Astronomical telescopes are normally built to optical and mechanical tolerances such that the tremor or seeing disk caused by atmospheric turbulence sets the limit of performance; that is, the instrumental blurring of a point star image is less than the blurring caused by inhomogeneities in the earth's atmosphere above the telescope. Then the problem of registering a faint star image with a large telescope is one of contrast between the small angular patch representing the star (about 0.5 arc seconds in diameter under very good conditions) and a similar adjacent patch of blank night sky.

Under these conditions the brightness of the faintest object detectable with a specified degree of certainty in a given time does not improve in proportion to the collecting area of the telescope objective (all dimensions of the telescope being scaled in the same proportion), as would be expected in the presence of negligible sky background, but only in proportion to the square root of the area. (See, for example, *Astronomical Techniques*, University of Chicago Press, 1962, edited by W. A. Hiltner, Chapter 1 by W. A. Baum.) The same rule applies to photoelectric photometry of faint objects through a focal plane diaphragm, and to low-dispersion spectroscopy and spectrophotometry.

In most of the frontier problems the aim is to reach out to the most distant objects of each class. But for these faint objects the distance reached varies only as the square root of the diameter of the telescope, assuming the inverse-square law in transparent space and no redshift corrections; allowances for absorption and redshift will diminish the distance reached. The cost of telescopes varies as the square of the diameter for the sizes already built. For the "giant" telescopes not yet attempted, the cost may be expected to vary as rapidly as 2.5-3.0 power of the diameter, because of the increasing complexity of the design and high engineering costs. Thus, since the number of photons varies as the diameter squared, the cost per collected photon from such telescopes varies only as the 5/4 or 6/4 power of the diameter. But in view of the square-root relation between diameter and distance, the cost varies as the 5th or 6th power of the distance reached. (The cost varies as the 5/3 or 6/3 power of the volume of space opened to exploration.)

For medium- and high-resolution spectroscopy, where the light of the night sky does not enter as a background illumination, the gain with telescopes of larger aperture does vary as the square of the diameter, provided the collimator of the spectrograph increases in proportion to the diameter of the telescope. (See, e.g., Baum, previous reference, or Bowen, Chapter 2 in same volume.) But if the collimator diameter remains unchanged, the gain with telescope size varies at best as the square root of the aperture, and for unwidened spectra there is no gain at all. Single-diffraction gratings large enough to meet the desired condition are not available even for the existing 200-inch telescope. For a 400-inch telescope, a grating area 24 to 30 inches in diameter would be required for proper efficiency, and such a size is beyond present-day technology. The obvious corollary to these conclusions is that successful engineering development of much larger gratings would be as effective in increasing the aperture of the objective, even with existing telescopes, as is discussed further in the section on auxiliary instruments. Such development is an essential preliminary to building still larger instruments.

Other factors besides aperture have something to offer in extending the working limit of a large telescope. Longer exposure times will, for a linear quantum detector, produce a gain that varies as the square root of the time invested; with photographic plates the situation is complicated by saturation and reciprocity failure. The limit can be extended in proportion to the square root of the gain in quantum efficiency. Such a gain may be realized from a practical image tube or from improved photographic emulsions; the efficiency is low enough at present so that there is room for a gain at least as great as that from doubling the telescope aperture. Better average seeing through the discovery of superior sites, or through treatment of the immediate surroundings of the telescope, is another obvious possibility. Here the gain is in direct proportion to the reduction in image diameter.

HOW BIG?

Any rational ten-year plan to provide facilities for the optical astronomers will inevitably put the major share of the funds into building large telescopes; partly because they are needed for frontier problems, and partly because experience has shown that the record of research yield from such telescopes over the whole range of observational astronomy has been an excellent return on the investment.

LARGE TELESCOPES

The Panel concluded that first priority should go to telescopes in the large-size category. Three large telescopes in the 150-200-inch aperture range should be funded as rapidly as meritorious proposals for their construction and operation are put forward. Proven designs should be used wherever possible, and at least one of the three should be located in the Southern Hemisphere. Each of the large telescopes placed at a new site should include a supporting auxiliary telescope. For the Southern Hemisphere site, this should be a 48-inch Schmidt-type survey instrument. This conclusion was based in the main on the consideration of urgency versus the long time-scale for the "giant x-inch."

In view of the rather slow gain in performance with size, an increase in aperture from the largest existing instrument (200 inches) to anything less than 350 or 400 inches would hardly be worth the investment needed to produce a new engineering design. If first priority were to be given to a "giant x-inch" in the 350-400-inch aperture range, the cost would be of the order of $100 million, and the time-scale would be five to seven years longer than for the straightforward construction of a proven design, such as that of the 200-inch Palomar telescope; i.e., the total time would be of the order of 15 years.

A second important consideration was the need for access to large telescopes by a much larger number of astronomers than is now possible, and the advantage of diversity and parallel advances on a number of fronts that would come with such increased access. It should be emphasized that the decision against construction of a "giant x-inch" at this time will not deny astronomers any suddenly breached threshold analogous to the creation of antiprotons by a particle accelerator, since the cutoff of any large telescope is not a sudden one.

The decision to recommend *three* such telescopes was dictated in part by the previously outlined need for acceleration of research on faint objects, and the fact that the number of large telescopes has not in recent years kept pace with the growth of the astronomical work force in the country. Three more such telescopes would double the number of U. S.-controlled large telescopes in the aperture range 100 to 200 inches. Since, as has been mentioned in earlier discussion, the number of astronomers in the United States is expected to double, at least, in the next decade, the number should not be any less. Consideration of the number of experienced operating groups that could undertake sizable projects of this kind, plus the size of the burden that would be placed on the instrumentally-inclined astronomers, sets an upper limit. In the opinion of the Panel, this limit is three.

LOCATION OF LARGE TELESCOPES

At least one of the three large telescopes should certainly be located in the Southern Hemisphere. The decision to have three large instruments makes it possible to serve more than one objective, by putting them at three different sites. And the immediate construction from a proven design can shorten the interval until a U. S.-controlled telescope of major size can bring in observations of the unique and underexploited riches of the southern sky: the nearest external galaxies (the Magellanic Clouds), the center of our own galaxy passing near the zenith, the nearest globular clusters. The existing imbalance, with the seven largest telescopes in the world all in the Northern Hemisphere and the two 74-inch instruments in the Southern Hemisphere at inferior sites, may soon be redressed in part under European auspices. Whatever other countries may do, it would seem logical for the United States to set up a Southern Hemisphere telescope that will bring to the southern skies the same power and versatility that the highly successful 200-inch Palomar telescope has provided in the Northern Hemisphere.

Unless telescopes in the 150-200 inch aperture range are located at the most favorable sites, their potential usefulness can be seriously degraded. In the United States, climatological factors make it imperative that large telescopes be located in the southwestern part of the country. Thorough investigation of temperature, wind, clear night hours, transparency, darkness of the sky, and especially seeing is required before a new site is occupied, in the United States as elsewhere. Considerations of convenience or proximity to urban centers are secondary to finding a site of superior quality.

UNDER WHAT AUSPICES?

The Panel has not attempted to select specific institutions for each optical telescope that it recommends to be built. Such designations by the Panel could have created conflict-of-interest situations that would have prevented qualified astronomers from serving on the Panel.

For each class of instrument, proposals will undoubtedly be put forward by universities, research institutions, or associations of universities. For the larger instruments at least, and particularly in cases where a choice must be made, *ad hoc* evaluation panels should be established to review proposals. The Panel has given thought to the general principles to be followed in selecting the organization to build and operate the telescopes of largest aperture.

Previous Performance

Competence, demonstrated by building a telescope of lesser aperture and producing research results with it, constitutes an essential qualification. The alertness and breadth of experience of the astronomers associated with the organization must be weighed. The group must have shown itself capable of developing auxiliary instruments that work well and of maintaining them in optimum condition.

Type of Institution

There is no single answer as to the type of organization best suited to be the builder and custodian of a large optical telescope. In this, as in quite a number of this country's other educational, cultural, and scientific enterprises, the strength that comes from diversity and friendly rivalry would appear to give the best guarantee of outstanding achievement.

Since optical astronomy requires a good climate, there were strong reasons for establishing the Kitt Peak National Observatory, a national center operated by an association of universities. Such an organization can engage in activities unsuited to the cloudy surroundings of excellent universities in the eastern part of the country, and too large for any one of them to manage alone. The nationwide character of such a center, and its status as a federally financed facility open to all qualified applicants, combine to guarantee that access to its telescopes will be granted to the less-well-established workers. Such a center must, of course, have a large telescope, and until it does, it cannot completely fulfill its objectives. The 150-inch reflector already planned by the Kitt Peak National Observatory should be completed at the earliest practical date. This enterprise, approved by the National Science Foundation, is counted as one of the three large telescopes recommended by the Panel.

Certain single universities with experience in the operation of an observatory are quite likely to ask to be assigned the responsibility of building a large telescope. Where the qualifications can be demonstrated beyond doubt, there need be no hesitation about singling out a particular university in this way. When the funds of the federal government go into such a project, the operating institution cannot have sole proprietary rights, but must administer the new astronomical resource as a national asset, granting a portion of observing time to qualified observers from other institutions. Nevertheless, the more intimate association of such a telescope with an astronomical staff connected with a single institution could favor the planning of a sustained and concentrated research campaign, when such is needed. And the fact that the home team of observers would be faculty members in a university, who taught courses and had thesis students, would give a chance for the large telescope to exert its maximum influence on the educational process, even though the graduate students did not themselves have access to the instrument.

Decisions between competing universities, or between single universities and associations, must be grappled with by the *ad hoc* committee that considers all the factors for each large facility. The most important requirement, in the Panel's view, is free and open competition. The inter-university association or national center is a valuable device for enabling universities to do collectively what no one of them can do as well, or at all, by itself. But there should not be any automatic, unreviewed preemption by such centers of functions that can be carried out as well or better in the universities. Each assignment should be made on the merits.

The Primary Goal

The decisions to be taken in locating the largest and most expensive optical telescopes must be directed to the primary goal—acceleration of astronomical research on the most difficult frontier problems. The quality of the people who build and administer the new facilities, and particularly the quality of the observers selected to use them—seasoned veterans, young developing astronomers, and promising postdoctoral fellows—are more important than the organizational structure or the management scheme. More than one arrangement has been made to work well by the nuclear physicists in the operation of particle accelerators. But whatever schemes are adopted to bring the nation's largest telescopes and talented astronomers together, the principle of equality of opportunity must, at this level, be subordinated to an insistence on performance—to the requirement of excellence at the top.

ENGINEERING STUDY FOR A GIANT TELESCOPE

The Panel recommends that as soon as the three large telescopes for the next decade are under way, a representative study group be assembled to consider the problems of building a telescope of the largest feasible size, to decide on practical design concepts, and to prepare a cost estimate for the design adopted.

There can hardly be any doubt of the ultimate desirability of planning for an optical telescope larger than any yet built. Yet, for the reasons given in our discussion of performance and size (p. 40), the next upward step cannot be a small one if a sizable gain in depth-penetrating power is to be realized. A thoroughgoing engineering design study to determine the feasibility and cost of a 400-inch or possibly 600-inch telescope ought to be undertaken before any proposal to start such a project is seriously considered.

The problems to be considered are both optical and mechanical. What material should be used for the mirror and what technique for fabrication and for producing the final precise shape? What focal ratio is practical and how shall the enormous surface be supported so as to hold its proper shape at all pointing angles? Will transportation problems preclude making the mirror from the raw material at any other place than the observing site? Can the mechanically desirable shift to an alt-azimuth mounting—now standard for large radio telescopes—be made without loss of following and pointing accuracy? Can the flexure in the very heavy mounting be balanced out, or compensated by corrections introduced through a computer?

Since the enterprise would, in the end, undoubtedly be one of national scope, the Association of Universities for Research in Astronomy (AURA) would be an appropriate agency under which to organize the study. The study group should include observational astronomers, optical experts, and mechanical and structural engineers of the highest competence.

TELESCOPES OF MODERATE SIZE

The Panel recommends that *four* general-purpose telescopes of aperture range 60 to 84 inches be built in the next ten years. These are self-sufficient telescopes, and are in addition to the supporting telescopes mentioned as auxiliaries to the large instruments discussed on page 42.

The same considerations of performance versus size that create difficulties for astronomers contemplating the construction of telescopes larger than any yet built are favorable to the users of telescopes of intermediate size, here defined as 60 to 84 inches aperture. Experience with such instruments at good sites (such as the Mount Wilson Observatory and the McDonald Observatory) shows them to be capable of turning out first-rate research on problems where the rate of photon collection may be less than that from the largest existing telescopes; examples were cited on page 17. Such telescopes are large enough to support the complete range of analyzing instruments. Whenever one of them can be used for observational work that would otherwise consume time on one of the largest telescopes, the opportunities for access to the latter are multiplied. Instrumental developments may be tested and later transferred to the largest telescope after they have proven their worth.

Proven designs for telescopes of intermediate size exist, but, where required, a modified design would not involve high engineering costs. Instruments of this size cost a great deal, however, and their capabilities are such that they should be located only at good sites. The conditions need not be as stringent as for the largest telescopes, but universities in the cloudy eastern or midwestern parts of the country, which have strong astronomy departments and could qualify as productive operators of intermediate-size telescopes on the basis of existing observational programs, must consider putting them at observing stations in the West or Southwest. Often this could be on or adjacent to an already-occupied site.

Universities in the western or southwestern part of the country with well-established astronomy departments can put forward a strong case for intermediate-size telescopes. Here suitable nearby sites can be found, and the easy integration of the telescopes into graduate-student thesis problems can be a very important part of the development and training of new astronomers. Universities or research institutions already operating good telescopes of intermediate size or larger should not be excluded from consideration for an additional telescope in the 60-84-inch range if the entire case, based on site, productivity, and educational benefits, is a strong one.

The recommendation of *four* telescopes is dictated again by the number of institutions with the proper capability and background. There are now five U. S. telescopes in this aperture range at good-climate sites.

SMALL TELESCOPES

The Panel recommends that *eight* telescopes of 36 to 48 inches aperture be built in the next decade. These should be fully equipped research instruments located at dark-sky sites near universities with active graduate departments. Climatic conditions need be given little weight.

The case for modern telescopes of research quality as an integral part of the basic local equipment of an institution maintaining a graduate-level astronomy department has been set forth in Section II. The effectiveness of the concept has been demonstrated at several institutions in relatively poor or mediocre climates, of which Wisconsin, Michigan, and Case Institute have been cited as examples. While the 36-to-48-inch aperture range is given, the most useful design thus far has been a 36-inch Cassegrain reflector, equipped with a photoelectric photometer, a low-dispersion spectrograph, and possibly a spectrum scanner. Telescopes in this category are now almost "off-the-shelf" items, and need not be re-engineered in each case.

Some of the institutions acquiring these telescopes may be acquiring their first instruments with research capabilities. The qualification should be an existing graduate department of demonstrated vitality; at least one faculty member in it should have some aptitude and experience in observational astronomy and the use of instruments.

The recommendation of *eight* such telescopes is based on the number already existing and an estimate of the number of astronomy departments that are likely to come forward with meritorious proposals. The recent rapid development of graduate study in astronomy in universities that previously had only small programs or did not award the Ph.D. degree in astronomy at all makes it probable that the decade ahead will see similar developments at several more institutions. Thus it is possible that *eight* such telescopes will, toward the end of the decade, prove to be too few. If the sufficient number of small telescopes for institutions meeting the qualifications set forth here should prove to be *twelve* rather than *eight,* or even a larger number, the added cost would still be only a small percentage of the total expenditure recommended by the Panel, and well within the margin of error.

It should be emphasized that the instruments in the 36 to 48 inches aperture range are research telescopes. Additional teaching telescopes of, say, 16 to 30 inches may appropriately be funded from provisions for graduate laboratory equipment, which are not within the province of this Panel.

SUMMARY OF RECOMMENDATIONS FOR OPTICAL TELESCOPES

1   *Three* large telescopes of the 150-to-200-inch class. The Kitt Peak projected 150-inch is included as one of the instruments. The other two should be of 200-inch diameter, and at least one should be located in the Southern Hemisphere. Only the very best mountain-top sites can be considered for location. Cost: $60 million.

2   A study group to be formed as soon as the three large telescopes are well under way, to consider the design of the largest feasible optical reflector. Cost estimate: $1.0 million spread over four years.

3   *Four* moderate-size telescopes of 60-to-84-inch aperture to be located in above-average climatic sites. Universities with strong astronomy departments or research institutions with exceptional promise or past achievement would be the recipients. Cost: $4.0 million.

4   *Eight* fully equipped modern reflecting telescopes of 36 to 48 inches to be located at well-organized astronomy departments at good universities. Cost: $3.2 million.

The estimated cost of this four-part construction and study program, based on the detailed engineering data of Section VI and the Appendix, is thus $68.2 million, with no operating expense included.

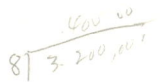

IV A PROGRAM FOR CONSTRUCTION OF RADIO TELESCOPES

In the first two sections of this report we have discussed the scientific problems presented to radio astronomy and the instrumental specifications demanded by them. It was shown that existing instrumentation is inadequate to perform effective work on these programs; nevertheless, it was found that the technical knowledge exists to build instruments that can reach beyond the thresholds of information now foreseen. It was found that instruments of extremely high resolution were required, and also versatile instruments of considerably greater capacity than those now in existence. Along with these, a group of lesser instruments useful in special problems and for student training is required. This section of the report presents the specific recommendations of the Panel as to the radio telescopes that it believes represent a reasonable and prudent goal for the next decade.

A MAJOR HIGH-RESOLUTION INSTRUMENT

In the discussion in Sections I and II, it has been shown that the primary need in radio astronomy is a very powerful high-resolution instrument. This is needed particularly for the study of the physics of the bright extragalactic radio sources, and for cosmological studies, and also for other programs in galactic structure and solar-system phenomena. For reasons already given, especially the need for detailed study of the bright extragalactic sources, this instrument must, as its prime goal, achieve a resolution of less than 10 seconds of arc at centimeter wavelengths. Its collecting area must be adequate to allow the detection of sources so faint that about 25 sources can be detected in each square degree of sky. The size and distribution of its energy-collecting area must be such that sidelobe responses can be suppressed to a satisfactory level. As a secondary goal, the instrument should, if feasible, achieve high quality, extremely low sidelobes, and pencil-beam performance with a resolution of about one minute of arc at 21-cm wavelength, for use in studies of galactic structure.

The Panel recommends, as the largest single undertaking in radio astronomy, the construction of a large array that would achieve these goals. Such an array might consist, for example, of about 100 separate parabolic antennas, each perhaps 85 feet in diameter. Each should have a surface quality giving good operation down to wavelengths as short as 3 cm. These antennas may be placed in a single line, utilizing the rotation of the earth to move them, in effect, along a second coordinate on the sky. Or they might be arranged in the pattern of a cross. Other possibilities may prove effective, and the engineering of the array should include a search for a format that will give maximum returns. When the antennas are spaced so as to give one-minute-of-arc resolution at 21 cm, about 10 per cent of the aperture would be filled, leading to extremely low sidelobe levels. When the antennas are spaced so as to give resolutions of less than 10 seconds of arc, the aperture filling will be considerably less than 1 per cent, and special procedures, of the kind outlined in Section II, will be required to provide adequate sidelobe suppression. Every effort should be made to include as high a degree of versatility as can be achieved without increasing costs unreasonably.

It is expected that a project of this magnitude will cost $40 million. The cost is fairly predictable, since 85-foot paraboloids of the specified surface accuracy have now been built many times and several engineering and construction firms have proved their competence (see Table A, Appendix, p. 90). Likewise there is considerable experience in interferometry between single pairs of such dishes over a long baseline. The earth's atmosphere and ionosphere do not introduce appreciable departures from phase coherence, as shown by tests at Jodrell Bank in England at a wavelength of 1.9 meters, over a baseline of 70 miles. Control of line-lengths and phase stability has been tested at the Owens Valley Radio Observatory at wavelengths of 31 cm and 12 cm, and in a more limited way at the National Radio Astronomy Observatory at Green Bank at a wavelength of 10 cm. A precise line-length monitoring system, based on signals sent out from the central receiving point, has been used on the Stanford 32-element array. In all these tests, stability adequate to give an angular resolution of two seconds of arc was demonstrated.

Although there is little doubt about the basic feasibility of the large high-resolution array, and although the performance of the entire system may be predicted with some confidence, the replication of so many components, even though each is of a proven design, and the tying together of the signal lines from all the widely spaced receiving points make the whole undertaking a very complex one. The project thus appears to be beyond the capabilities of a single university, and, in fact, falls naturally into the category of instruments that should be constructed by the National Radio Astronomy Observatory. Since this will be a major national endeavor, the National Radio Astronomy Observatory should make every effort to avail itself of the knowledge and experience in the required techniques possessed by the scientific community. Means should be provided for extensive participation by scientists who are not members of the NRAO staff in the planning and development of the instrument. It may take little less than a decade to build, and so should be started as soon as possible.

A HIGH-RESOLUTION ARRAY OF LIMITED CAPABILITY

Going beyond the major instrument proposed above, the Panel feels that the need for high resolution is great enough to warrant proposal of an alternative, simpler, less expensive, and quicker approach to the high-resolution problem *per se*. It is highly desirable to have an instrument that can achieve quite high resolution on the brighter radio sources. This would provide many advantages: 1) Some prime data would be forthcoming at the earliest possible time; 2) these data would be valuable guides to the design of the giant high-resolution antenna; 3) this antenna would provide a testing ground for techniques possibly useful to the high-resolution antenna, such as methods of sidelobe suppression and the interconnection of various energy-collecting elements.

To implement this need, the Panel recommends the funding of the already-proposed extension of the observing facilities at the Owens Valley Observatory of the California Institute of Technology. This proposed extension can be achieved relatively quickly, and will produce high-resolution measurements on a limited number of radio sources. The extension includes the construction of four new steerable parabolic reflectors of about 130-foot aperture, bringing to six the number of antennas at the site, and an increase in the length of the interferometer track on which the antennas are carried.

Based on existing data, it appears virtually certain that the presently approved, but unfunded, additions will prove highly successful. In this case, a further increase in the available equipment by a factor of about two will allow useful resolutions of less than 10 seconds of arc, the specification set previously in this report. Thus, the Panel feels that one should anticipate now the need for this further addition to the Owens Valley facilities. The cost of the approved extension to the Owens Valley system has been carefully estimated to be about $5 million; the second extension recommended here would cost about the same amount. Therefore, the total funding required for this development is $10 million. It should perhaps be emphasized that this instrument is not an adequate substitute for the giant telescope previously recommended; but it will serve as an effective interim instrument and guide to optimum design of the very large array, and continue to be useful in its own right. Since the very large array will take almost a decade to build, construction should be commenced immediately. The results from the extension at the Owens Valley Observatory can be expected to come in good time to contribute to the final success of the very large array.

LARGE PARABOLOIDS

It was shown in Section II that there is a great need for additional powerful, multi-purpose, easily used instruments to complement the high-resolution instruments proposed above. These are required for 21-cm galactic studies, polarization studies, measurements of source spectra, monitoring of variable cosmic radio sources and planets, and radar experiments, among other projects. They should be quickly convertible from one type of observation to another, and adaptable to radar operation by addition of a transmitter. The growth in manpower, and problems to which such instruments are applicable, indicate a national need for more than one development of this nature. It would appear that the appropriate instrument for these tasks is the fully steerable paraboloid of about 300-foot diameter, with a surface accuracy adequate for 10-cm or shorter wavelengths. Any smaller instrument is not sufficiently powerful; a larger instrument encounters severe technical and financial obstacles. After due consideration, the Panel feels that the appropriate number of such instruments to be built within the next ten years is two. Progress with any less would be too slow; any more might well exceed the foreseeable observational requirements and manpower availability.

The cost of each of these instruments will be $8 million, calling then for a total investment in such instruments of $16 million. These instruments could appropriately be built by a single university able to provide the extensive personnel support required, by a regional group of universities, or by the NRAO. It would be desirable if at least one of these were constructed adjacent to one of the large arrays previously proposed, since electrical interconnection of the array and the large paraboloid may offer unique observational capabilities of great value in some problems. Since three years or more will be required to complete these instruments, once started, their construction should be authorized at the earliest possible time.

SMALLER SPECIAL-PURPOSE INSTRUMENTS

In addition to the major costly instruments recommended above, the Panel feels strongly that both an adequate program in radio astronomy and the proper support of student training call for extensive investment in lesser instruments over the next ten years. These will be, in general, instruments aimed at special problems, often of an exploratory nature, and will normally be located at universities active in graduate education. The Panel does not consider it proper to specify all the instruments required; in many specific cases, the form of a required instrument will develop naturally from the special interests and areas of competence of the proposers of the instrument. In fact, it should be emphasized that the specifications of many of the instruments to be built cannot be predicted today. The past history of radio astronomy has shown that we are still in a stage of development in which many of the more important celestial phenomena and observing techniques are yet to be discovered. Examples from the recent past of such new developments include the detection of the quasi-stellar sources, radio emission from flare stars, and the use of lunar occultations to achieve resolution.

Nevertheless, the Panel sees some areas in which significant instruments are clearly justified, and presents these here as examples of suitable projects for support. These include large telescopes suitable for millimeter wavelengths; these may be steerable paraboloids up to 60 feet in diameter, and costing up to $2 million. Another example is improved arrays for the study of the decameter radiation of Jupiter and perhaps Saturn. Another is extended arrays for high-resolution studies of solar radiation. Telescopes particularly designed to monitor known flare stars would be most valuable. One of the larger university-operated paraboloids could be used as a radar system for studies of lunar and planetary surfaces and atmospheres, the interplanetary medium, and the motions of bodies in the solar system. In some cases, university departments will develop new and original electronic devices to be used in existing arrays or paraboloids. These may be perfected on a local antenna system during the development period, and later transferred to the major instruments at NRAO and other places; examples of the success of this procedure have already established a precedent. These devices may include special low-noise receivers, multi-channel receivers for hydrogen-line studies, receivers for the search for and/or study of other spectral lines, and radar astronomy instrumentation.

After due consideration, the Panel feels that approximately 15 universities will be capable of such projects over the next ten years. Based on estimates of the cost of the examples given, we estimate that the average cost to implement one of these projects will be about $2 million. Thus the Panel recommends that approximately $30 million be provided over the next ten years for projects of this nature. The limited power of such instruments should not be misconstrued as an indication that they are unimportant. In many cases, they will be capable of producing certain specific data beyond the capabilities of the giant instruments to produce; an example is the study of flare stars, to which the valuable time of the major instruments cannot be assigned. But more important, these lesser instruments will probably provide the principal practical experience to graduate students, and thus strongly influence the quality of personnel available in the latter portion of the decade. Thus they are of crucial importance, in that they will provide a training ground for the personnel who will be needed if the major instruments are to produce optimum results.

Indeed, the Panel feels that particular emphasis must be given to the continuing support of radio astronomy groups in the universities. Although annual operating support for existing programs is outside the scope of this report (see Section VI, p. 76), the Panel reports its opinion that the present level of support of university departments with on-going radio astronomy programs is less than adequate. This situation has arisen perhaps because universities have had to assume the operation of large and rather complex new research instruments over a short interval of time, and have had to rely heavily on extramural support in a new field of research that has not been integrated into the traditional academic structure in the same way as has optical astronomy. In the opinion of the Panel, there is already danger of an imbalance between the strong federal support given to the national center for radio astronomy, on the one hand, and, on the other hand, the support given to the varied activities in the same field in the universities.

The effectiveness of the support to university departments would be markedly increased if it were in the form of long-term block-funding rather than on an annual basis, as is now the common practice. Long-term funding will enable the universities to retain effective staffs and to carry out time-consuming development programs extending over a number of years.

DESIGN STUDY FOR THE LARGEST POSSIBLE STEERABLE PARABOLOID

The Panel, after considerable discussion with a broad segment of the radio-astronomy community, feels that, by the end of the decade, a need may arise for fully steerable paraboloids even larger than the 300-foot paraboloids previously proposed in this report. The basis for this opinion is the present youthful state of radio astronomy, a situation in which it has been found, as can be supported by many events in recent history, that many important phenomena are yet to be discovered. Throughout the short history of radio astronomy, every increase in telescope size has resulted in the discovery of new and very important phenomena in the universe. It is realistic to assume that this sequence of events will continue as the major instruments described here are brought into service. The extension of the large high-resolution arrays may be made simply by adding to them more collecting elements of the same type as those originally used in the array. Thus, no great difficulty is foreseen in extending these instruments, should the need become apparent. However, an increase in the size of large paraboloids requires extensive design and engineering studies, since each increase in size confronts the builder with new technological obstacles.

When paraboloids larger than 300 feet in diameter are studied, severe technical problems are encountered and the possible solutions are quite complex, including, for example, the use of servo-operated controls on the shape of the reflector surface. The design and evaluation of these solutions are costly and very time-consuming, as has been shown in the unsuccessful attempt at Sugar Grove to build a 600-foot paraboloid. Clearly, construction of a successful giant telescope for astronomical purposes requires a thorough-going engineering study. If the reasonable assumption is made that toward the end of the decade a need for paraboloids larger than 300 feet in diameter will have appeared, studies of possible antenna designs should be commenced in the not-too-distant future.

Thus the Panel recommends that design studies for the largest feasible steerable paraboloids be commenced at an early date. The control of the reflector surface through a servo system should be investigated in the course of this study. The funding probably required to make an adequate study, as here proposed, is $1 million.

A SOLAR RADAR SYSTEM

The possibility of using radar techniques to produce unique data on the solar corona has now been demonstrated. Such studies could contribute important data on solar phenomena, especially when used in conjunction with passive radio observations of the active sun. However, such an installation would cost perhaps $15 million, and the Panel considers that the data per dollar that might accrue from such an installation are not commensurate with the data per dollar to be produced by the instruments proposed above. Furthermore, since such installations have had practical utility for space and military operations, they have hitherto found sources of funds through agencies that do not ordinarily contribute to conventional astronomical instrumentation. Therefore, the Panel does not wish to recommend that funding of such a radar system should be considered within the framework of the present report.

SUMMARY OF RECOMMENDATIONS FOR RADIO TELESCOPES

1   A very-high-resolution array with great collecting area and low side-lobe levels. Construction time, approximately one decade. Cost: $40 million.

2   Two additions to the interferometer at the Owens Valley Observatory of the California Institute of Technology. Six years to complete. Cost: $10 million.

3   Two fully steerable 300-foot paraboloids. Five years to complete. Cost: $16 million.

4   Smaller special-purpose instruments, approximately 15, costing an average of $2 million each. $30 million.

5   Design study of largest feasible steerable paraboloid. Cost: $1 million. The cost of this five-part program for radio astronomy thus totals $97 million, not including operating expense.

V AUXILIARY INSTRUMENTS AND AUTOMATION

AUXILIARY INSTRUMENTS

Although the telescope is properly given great emphasis as the single most important tool of the observational astronomer, the analyzing devices and the radiation detectors at the focus of the telescope are so vital a link in the process of collecting and decoding the information being received from astronomical bodies that they deserve the closest scrutiny. A review of current practice and performance in this area of technology indicates that very appreciable gains over present operations are possible. Any rational division of the time, talent, and money to be invested in improved observing facilities over the next decade must certainly make adequate provision for research and development in this field, and for equipping both old and new telescopes with modern auxiliaries.

Improvement in the performance of a detector or analyzing instrument has the same effect as increasing the aperture of a telescope, and because the point has now been reached where the optical and mechanical specifications of telescopes, both radio and optical, are so well understood that no great improvement in efficiency seems likely, it is particularly important to improve the efficiency of the analyzing instruments used at the end of the telescope. This is especially true because the cost of increasing the size of the telescope aperture is enormously greater than the probable cost of improving the efficiency of photometers, spectrographs, and direct-plate cameras, and the same gain in threshold detection of celestial objects is achievable by either route.

Increased effectiveness of existing telescopes through improved auxiliaries is not, however, an argument against new large telescopes, or against considering the design of one larger than any previously built, since any expansion of the calculated horizon of these expensive instruments will bring in a flood of data previously unobservable by any method. This new information is almost certain to contain revealing surprises.

The general areas of investigation that give promise of a gain in efficiency are:

Radiation Detectors

The detectors used on optical telescopes are, for the most part, quantum detectors, and the ultimate limit of one recorded event for each incident photon, with negligible spurious background, is an obvious standard against which to compare current performances.

Photographic plates. The highest published value of the measured quantum efficiency of a photographic emulsion is about 1 per cent, but, at the very low intensities encountered in astronomical use, the same accumulated incident energy produces less blackening than under normal testing conditions (reciprocity failure), and the efficiency is several times smaller. Working astronomers in several observatories have shown by experimentation with baking of plates, refrigeration during exposure, and pre-flashing, that appreciable improvement is possible. What is needed is a full investigation into the mechanism of reciprocity failure at low intensities, and of possible increases in the fundamental efficiency of photographic emulsions under conditions of astronomical use. A similar campaign by the photographic industry, directed toward corrections of high-intensity reciprocity failure (a campaign inspired by commercial and military requirements), brought speed gains of 20 to 100 times. On the other hand, there have been no significant improvements in astronomical emulsions in 15 years.

Photoelectric cathodes. Quantum efficiencies of 15 to 25 per cent are commonly realized in the blue and ultraviolet; the yield falls by an order of magnitude in going to the deep red, and by another factor of five or so in the near-infrared. A determined search for photoelectrically sensitive materials with higher efficiency in the red and infrared is worth supporting.

Image tubes. The bright prospect held out by the considerably higher quantum efficiency of the photoelectric cathode relative to the photographic plate has not been realized after several years' effort. In only a few limited special cases, results not attainable by photography have been achieved; yet progress has been made. Unless phenomenal improvements in photographic emulsions are realized, a gain of 10 to 20 times is still technologically feasible. This very great prize is worth multiplying the sizable investment already made several times over.

Infrared detectors. Excellent detectors of both the photoconductive and bolometer types are now available. The problems in adapting them to astronomical uses are mainly problems of cryogenic and thermal engineering to reduce ambient radiation, and, at the longer wavelengths, finding a way of compensating for variable thermal radiation from the atmosphere. (See "Sky radiation," p. 61.) The very promising initial efforts at two or three observatories should be given vigorous continuing support, and entrance of other technologically competent groups into this field should be encouraged.

Radio receivers. As a result of many improvements in radio receivers for radio telescopes, including the parametric amplifier and the maser, one may presently come within a factor of about five of the ultimate sensitivity possible in ground-based radio telescopes. However, such excellent performance is presently available with only a few radio telescopes. The remaining noise is mainly thermal radiation from components ahead of the receiver, in the circuit, and the atmosphere, and not noise generated in the receiver itself. The support of instrumentation in this field must therefore have two objectives: 1) the development of telescopes approaching very closely the ultimate sensitivity permitted by the atmosphere and cosmic radio emission; and 2) the outfitting of more radio telescopes with the rather complicated and fairly expensive electronic equipment required to attain low-noise performance.

Auxiliary Optical Instruments

The narrow slit. In most spectroscopic observations, particularly those at moderate and high dispersion, there is a loss of efficiency because much of the star image does not go through the narrow slit. A large gain in efficiency appears possible through the following developments:

Diffraction gratings. Theory shows that an increase in the size of the collimator is just as effective as the same proportionate increase in the aperture of the telescope. However, diffraction gratings large enough to handle the larger collimator beam are not now available. Development of ruling engines capable of producing gratings at least twice as large as those now in use (6 to 8 inches) would be a very profitable investment. Increasing the angular dispersion by developing gratings that maintain their efficiency in higher orders, or by going to the echelle grating, may also be effective.

Interferometric spectrometers. The Fabry-Perot etalon has a large entrance pupil, good luminous efficiency, and extremely high spectral resolution. Its use in astronomy for detailed studies of limited regions of the spectrum has been exploited in only a limited way. The potential of Michelson-type moving-mirror interference spectrometers, particularly in the infrared, is not yet fully explored.

Fast cameras. The Schmidt camera, as used in spectrographs, although giving excellent definition at low f-ratios, is not well adapted to light detectors, other than the photographic plate, because larger pieces of apparatus mounted "in the beam" block out too much light. If image tubes become the standard recorders of faint spectra, there will be an overwhelming need for a high-resolution camera that has a focal surface external to all the optical elements and a focal ratio no greater than 1.0, and that can be made in apertures of 12 inches or more.

Atmospheric Disturbances

Seeing. For most types of observations, halving the angular diameter of the seeing disk of a star is equivalent to doubling the aperture of the telescope. While the empirical search for sites with favorable proportions of nights with good seeing must be continued, the whole problem should be put on a firmer basis by broader and more fundamental investigations. There should be a much greater effort at understanding the physics of seeing, its relation to terrain and meteorological factors, its variation with height above the ground, and possible improvements from control of dome temperature and air flow, or from modification of ground cover around the dome. Here again the prize is great enough to justify a considerable investment.

Sky radiation. The night-sky brightness (or airglow) sets the final limit to all observations with ground-based optical telescopes. Although there is no known way to eliminate this light, there are developments that would reduce the effect of variations in the brightness that raise the noise level in photoelectric comparison of stars and adjacent sky, or introduce fluctuations into infrared measurements. Similar difficulties occur in radio astronomy measurements at wavelengths below 3 cm, where water vapor in the atmosphere introduces variable opacity. Dual channels, differential measurements, and the choice of a signal-modulation frequency low in noise content are possible approaches. For the infrared and radio wavelengths, choice of a site can also make a large difference.

The examples cited in the previous paragraphs represent some of the more persistent obstacles in the way of making telescopes deliver the ultimate performance permitted by the laws of optics and radiation. Unpredictable technological developments or new ideas not now foreseen may alter the prospects considerably in less than a decade, and dictate support of instrumental developments of an entirely different character. The support given to such projects must be kept flexible and be subjected to periodic reassessment.

Recommendations

1   The fraction of the total astronomical research effort actively devoted to instrumental development should be increased by a factor of two in the next few years. Funds of the order of $1 million a year will be needed.

2   The support should go to the major observatories and university astronomy departments, since development must be carried on close to the actual observations and other processes of astronomy to be kept realistic. A separate special laboratory for the development of instruments should not be created, since it would lack this close connection.

3   National observatories, such as Kitt Peak, will quite appropriately build up a group of astronomers, engineers, and physicists devoted to instrumental development and testing. It would be a mistake, however, not to have specialist groups at several observatories or universities attacking various facets of instrumental problems.

4   In many cases the observatory-connected investigator will devote a good part of his primary grant to subcontracts with industrial laboratories. As an astronomer end-user, who knows what is needed, he will guide the work and test the products that come out of it. Examples might be photographic plates and image tubes. Budgetary support must be adequate to assure more than desultory attention from the industrial laboratory involved.

AUTOMATION

Introduction

The essential continuing requirement facing us is the requirement for more data. Many problems require more observing time on moderate- and large-size telescopes. But every link in the chain of data-acquisition must be scrutinized to see that a system of the greatest possible efficiency is used, guaranteeing that every datum is recorded and available.

In the first part of this section we have dealt with auxiliary equipment used with telescopes and with the all-important detectors used to turn incoming photons into usable data. The remaining link in the data chain, having to do with data-processing and evaluation, also requires substantial increases in efficiency in the use of time and manpower.

Astronomy is just emerging into the modern era of automatic control. The information content that must be processed for many astronomical problems is exceedingly large, approaching that of high-energy physics. The techniques for automatic data-handling are in many cases already developed; wherever and whenever the efficiency and accuracy of acquiring or processing data can be improved, the opportunities should be vigorously exploited.

Only a few optical telescopes are even partially automated, either in their basic operation or for final data-reduction. On the other hand, radio astronomers are already making wide use of modern data-processing techniques, and the revolution is well advanced. Existing radio telescopes are being fitted with modern readout and computer equipment as rapidly as funding permits; costs for proposed new radio facilities routinely include provision for the instrumentation needed for automation. But in optical astronomy a marked increase in the over-all output of fundamental data is clearly possible.

Observatories embarking on a program looking toward the realization of such objectives will require the services of engineers experienced in instrumentation and data-processing; the larger observing centers must think of persons technically competent in this field as a normal part of their resident staffs. The drain on the engineering community to provide the relatively small number of engineers required would be almost negligible, but the impact on the astronomical community would be enormous. Among many other advantages, the acquisition of such engineers would free the time of astronomers who now do their own engineering work, so that they could proceed with the primary job of producing astronomical results.

Acquisition and Reduction of Data

In certain areas of astronomical research the available manpower and telescope time could be used to produce data much more efficiently if the burden of data-reduction were handled by machines rather than by hand. Programs that could be expedited in this way include: (1) those involving photographs or records of many stars obtained simultaneously, such as positions, proper motions, variable star magnitudes, objective prism spectral classification, and objective prism radial velocity determinations; (2) programs producing large quantities of simultaneous data on individual objects, such as multichannel photoelectric photometry, high-dispersion spectroscopy, and spectral scans of bright stars; (3) programs requiring two-dimensional intensity studies or isophotal plots of extended sources, such as galaxies and gaseous nebulae. An example of the possibilities is furnished by astrometric-reduction programs. Schemes already projected and nearing the stage of initial trial seem almost certain to keep reductions current with observation.

There are similar examples in radio astronomy of programs limited by reduction-time requirements: (1) repeated radio scans using multichannel hydrogen-line receivers to obtain radio isophotes of the distribution of neutral hydrogen in our galaxy or in neighboring galaxies; (2) analysis of spectral and temporal characteristics of radio bursts from the sun and planets; (3) analysis of occultations of radio sources by the moon or by the solar corona.

There is a second class of problems that are limited by available telescope time. Among these are: (1) direct photographs of very faint objects, (2) slit spectroscopic work for radial velocities or spectral classification of stars, (3) photon-limited single-channel photoelectric photometry or spectral scans, (4) observations requiring excellent seeing or atmospheric transparency. Although the most important gain in efficiency will come in the problems that are reduction-time limited, digitized and automated data-recording systems can not only improve the reliability and reduce the tedium of the observations that are telescope-time-limited, but also offer opportunities for optimum utilization of available quanta and the recovery of extremely weak signals otherwise submerged in the background. These techniques are well understood by the radio observers, and should be more generally exploited by optical observers.

A third possibility for improving efficiency comes when the observation time per object is comparable with or less than the setting time of the telescope. Then automatic setting of a rapidly moving telescope, a pre-programmed exposure schedule, and automatic digital readout of both positional data and the observational output will repay the cost many times. In all types of observations where the telescope output is an electrical signal or can be converted to one (photoelectric observations, infrared detectors, orthicon-type image tubes), direct digital readout not only reduces human errors but also presents the information in satisfactory form for rapid reduction by a computer.

Progress toward these desirable goals depends on support funds for those observatories that are willing and competent to undertake the responsibility of automating present astronomical facilities. Part of the funds would go for the employment of astronomical instrumentation engineers and associated technicians.

Development of New Automatic Instruments

Several of the possibilities for automated instruments mentioned above are already very close to realization, or could be adapted to astronomical measurements by a slight extension of techniques already known:

Automatic two-coordinate measuring engine. The astrometric measuring engine being installed at the Lick Observatory will be the first machine of this type. Precise x and y measurements can be made automatically from pre-programmed instructions stored on punched cards. Control by tape or a computer would be possible. Measurement of stellar magnitudes by an iris photometer is automatically included, and is reported out along with the coordinate readings on punched cards. Variations of the machine could include optional display of the measuring area where an auxiliary machine for pre-programming was not available or would not be efficient. A slight modification of the optics would permit conversion of the machine to a one-dimensional spectrum-plate-measuring engine.

Measuring engine-microphotometer for spectrum plates. Several possibilities, using principles tested separately, could be combined in an all-purpose analyzer for spectrum plates. For measurement of the position of the stellar-spectrum lines or comparison lines, visual displays aiding the centering of a line profile relative to a reference mark are already in use, with digital readout and data storage. Automation of the centering process and pre-programming of a set pattern of lines, as in a radial velocity program or in the measurement of stellar magnetic fields, would be feasible extensions. Where the intensity distribution across a spectrum line must be recorded, as in studies of line profiles or in equivalent width determinations for abundance studies, analog computers that allow for the calibrated characteristic curve of the plate are already in use. Transferral of the output from a strip-chart recording to digital form for processing in a computer can be accelerated by a digitized readout device. The final stage in automating the entire process is digital storage in a computer or on tape of the information in each spectrum-resolution bit, as has already been done on high-resolution solar spectrograms. The entire process would then become automatic and digital, with the strip-chart serving as a monitor and reference, but not as a link in the data-reduction.

Automatically controlled optical telescope. As a step on the way to the automated observatory outlined in a later paragraph, an automated telescope would not only provide a valuable proving ground, but also would be extremely useful in its own right. A small instrument could be programmed to carry out three-color extinction measurements on standard stars, thus saving observing time on major instruments and warning of deterioration of sky transparency. Atmospheric seeing and stellar scintillation could likewise be automatically recorded. A more important program would involve photoelectric programs on relatively bright stars involving either the standard three-color or narrow-band filter measurements. This would be a realization of the previously cited advantage of speeding up the routine in cases where the observation time for objects is less than the setting time.

Information Storage

The traditional solution to the need to store enormous volumes of data regarding the positions, the spectral types, the magnitudes and colors, the parallaxes and proper motions, and the binary character of hundreds of thousands of stars has been the issuance of specialized catalogues. These often become out-of-date before the enormous labor of revised editions can be completed, requiring recourse to scattered references in the literature. The advantages of data-storage on punched cards, with easy editing and insertion of new information, have already been resorted to at certain observatories, at least for specialized classes of objects, such as double stars. While the Panel does not suggest that such methods will replace the use of the printed page in conventional libraries as the principal medium of storage and communication, it does urge encouragement of central files of machine-stored data at a few major observatories that wish to undertake such projects. Such information can easily be printed out when needed, and can be exchanged in digital form, much as is now commonly done with computer programs. Information stored in this way, as on punched cards, is immediately applicable to automatic programming and to theoretical-analysis projects.

Automated Observatories

As the technology of automatic control systems advances to a state where more and more of the operations now under human control can be done under machine guidance, the time may be foreseen when almost all the procedures of data-acquisition and data-reduction used in observational astronomy may be carried out by automatic devices. An entirely automated observatory—a complex of telescopes, measuring engines, and other data-gathering instruments, together with a complex of plotters, printers, and other data display and output devices, all connected to a central computer and under the immediate and direct control of one or more observers—is now a definite possibility. Nearly all the work of any observatory falls into one of the following areas:

Routine observations. This area includes the repetitive work of astronomy that leads to the publication of lengthy catalogues and tables. The period of observation is long, and the work, tedious for human beings, should be handled automatically when possible.

Special observations. Here we find most of the spectacular work. For these programs only a modest amount of time (perhaps only a few nights) may be needed for the initial discovery. Automation is a less important factor in these first observations, but can be valuable in the extensive follow-up that is invariably necessary.

Monitoring observing conditions. Whenever possible, small auxiliary telescopes should be used to monitor the atmospheric transparency and steadiness, the general sky brightness, and other quantities of interest. The large instruments, relieved of such tasks, are thereby made more effective.

Data-processing. This area includes all the operations that are performed once a telescope provides output. Two types of data-processing can be thought of: (a) immediate data-display, permitting the observer to make quick decisions as to the best use of telescope time while he is still observing; (b) the detailed reduction of all the telescope output.

The automation equipment required for the postulated automatic observatory might consist of: (1) a central medium-size digital computer; (2) an individual control console for each major instrument; (3) a master control console from which minor instruments, including monitors, are normally controlled; (4) digital readouts for position of each instrument and digital readouts on all sensors where appropriate; (5) provision on all instruments for remote control of slewing motion, automatic guiding, focusing, switching of optical components, selecting of detectors, and adjusting apparatus; and (6) automatic measuring engines for fast and convenient readout of data, particularly from photographic plates.

The control console for each major instrument would be designed to permit the observer to control the telescope either directly from the console or indirectly through the central computer—a fast, core-memory model of moderate size. The computer occupies the central position in the system and communicates with the consoles and the telescopes. The digital readout systems can handle a wide variety of tasks, including automatic recording of the position of each instrument. This datum, together with the exact time, defines uniquely the position in the sky at which the telescope is pointed, and eliminates misidentification. Most electrical sensors lend themselves to digital readout; photographic plates, because they record such large quantities of data, can be processed efficiently only with automatic-measuring engines of the sort already described.

Recommendations

Initial support for the design and development of major instruments for automation of astronomical facilities should first be given to only a few experienced astronomical groups with qualified staffs. A fully automated pilot facility in each category can then be tested, evaluated, and finally made available to other observatories. Such an approach would help create standardization and avoid the growth of a hodge-podge of approaches. Already the Kitt Peak National Observatory, with support from the National

Aeronautics and Space Administration and the National Science Foundation, is well along in a plan for limited automatic operation of a single telescope of moderate size. Astronomers wishing to work in this general area should be required to become acquainted with this pioneer facility.

Surveys of existing commercial apparatus indicate that it would cost in the neighborhood of $2 million to fully automate a moderate-size observatory. This figure applies to an existing observatory that was not designed with automation in mind. New observatories could be automated for approximately half this amount.

The problem that now confronts both optical and radio observatories in the United States is, however, one of updating existing telescopes and data-analyzing equipment so that they will be partially automated and will present their output information in a form that can be fed directly into electronic computers. Well-conceived plans for step-by-step progress toward this goal should certainly be supported. Typical examples of instrumentation that will be needed include:

1 Readout, digitizing, and data-processing units to be attached to existing optical telescopes and plate-analysis instruments. These would cover pointing coordinates, photometer settings, photometer output, plate coordinates, and plate intensity readings. Digitizations of a single quantity may cost only a few thousand dollars; a complete readout system might come to $50,000 for instrumentation.

2 Fully automatic plate-measurement machines with automatic centering and provision for pre-programming for spectrum plates and direct photographs. These might cost $150,000 each. Pilot models will be more expensive.

3 Complete automation of a moderate-size optical telescope, including pre-programmed automatic setting and unattended acquisition of observational data.

4 Automation of telescope setting, observing routines, and data readout on existing radio telescopes.

The Panel has purposely refrained from assigning specific total dollar values to these categories, since experience in this rapidly developing field will come from pilot installations not yet in operation. Support of engineering and technical personnel needed to initiate and operate these programs in individual observatories constitutes part of the cost. Consideration of the unit costs already known and the advantages to be gained has led the Panel to recommend that a total of $10 million be allocated to these purposes in the next ten years. This is less than 5 per cent of the over-all sum recommended in this report; the potential gain in output is so great that the engineering of the automation of astronomical observations must be given high priority in the total effort.

VI THE MAGNITUDE OF THE PROGRAM

INTRODUCTION

This report recommends a program for construction of facilities that will utilize the versatile, relatively low-cost methods of ground-based astronomy to carry out the large fraction of the observations of the universe that can be done through the atmosphere, and thus to maintain the proper balance between the unique capabilities of instruments carried into space and the capabilities of those operated on the surface of the earth. The total cost for the ten-year program is less than the first five years of that part of the Space Administration's orbiting observatory program devoted to stellar astronomy and to radio astronomy. These orbiting observatories are, of course, only a small part of the whole space effort. The annual spending rate for the new ground-based facilities projected in the previous section of this report is of the order of one half of 1 per cent of the present total annual budget of the National Aeronautics and Space Administration.

Since astronomers represent a small fraction of the physical scientists in the country, however, it is appropriate to ask whether the ground-based facilities recommended represent a sharp acceleration in the next decade or are in line with growth rates already established or in sight.

In the case of optical astronomy, where there has been a long period of growth while the United States was establishing its dominant position in this area of science, it is possible to give a rough quantitative answer to this inquiry. The best single index of the nation's capability in observational optical astronomy would appear to be the collecting area of all its research telescopes. The necessary data have been taken from the Appendix of Kuiper and Middlehurst's *Telescopes* (University of Chicago Press, 1960), with a few additions for instruments completed since 1960. In Figure 20 is shown the integrated area of all telescopes of 24-inch aperture or larger in the United States. Accumulated totals at intervals of five to ten years are plotted. In the same figure is shown the breakdown for the size categories (large, medium, and small) as used in Section III and in the recommendations of this report. Here each point represents the new total after adding the telescopes completed in a given year. At the right side a hypothetical point is plotted on each of the graphs, showing how the collecting area in each of the four cases would stand in 1976 if all the recommendations of the Panel's report were completely implemented by that time. In no case is there any marked increase over the growth rate that has been established over previous decades. Implementation of the Panel's recommendations will do little more than keep up with the general trend, which indicates a doubling of the total collecting area each 15 years. Because there has been a slackening in the growth rate over the last 15 years, it is necessary, however, to compress about 15 years of normal growth into the next decade.

It will be noted that this long-term trend was established when the number of astronomers in the country was growing less rapidly than is now shown to be the case in the manpower survey in Section II (page 28). The manpower growth rate previously shown in Figure 18 (page 31) is reproduced at the top of the telescope-area graph in Figure 20. At the right edge is shown the range of the expected number of U. S. members of the International Astronomical Union in 1973, based on the projection of Table 2 (page 36), and the assumption that the ratio between the number of U. S. astronomers, as defined in Section II, and the number of U. S. members of the International Astronomical Union will continue to be about 3:2. The slope of this portion of the plot indicates a doubling of manpower in nine or ten years and increases more steeply than the projected growth of the telescope collecting area in any size category.

In summary, then, the optical facilities recommended by the Panel would appear to be reasonable and prudent. It should be noted that, even with full implementation of these recommendations, there will be fewer square feet of telescopic objective per U. S. astronomer at the end of the decade than there are now. And, even with some allowance for a slight reduction in the percentage of U. S. astronomers engaged in optical astronomy, as interest in theoretical astrophysics, radio astronomy, and space astronomy grows, the program is still based upon a straightforward projection. In view of the important contributions being made to the development of astronomy by observers with U. S. optical telescopes, to provide

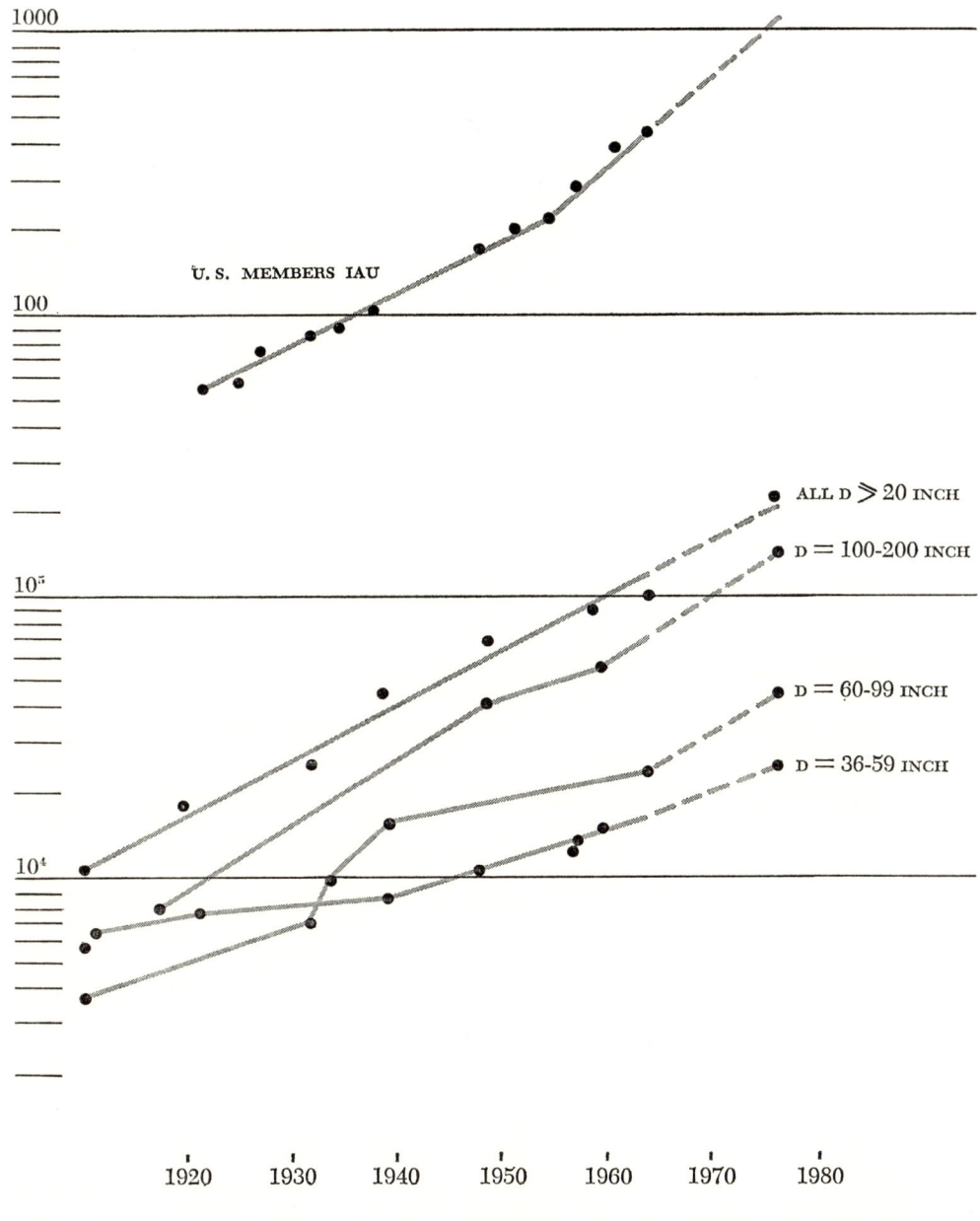

Figure 20
Growth of total collecting area of U.S. optical telescopes since 1910, projected to include facilities recommended by this report. The growth of the number of U.S. members in the International Astronomical Union is shown for comparison.

less than is recommended here would, in the opinion of the Panel, mean a loss of momentum, and would constitute a retrenchment.

There is no single index in radio astronomy that represents the ground-based observing potential in the United States, particularly since modern antenna systems consist of both arrays and paraboloids. The growth of the major U. S. facilities is barely a decade old, and no long-term trends or growth rates can be said to have been established. The recommendations of the Panel proposed a set of facilities demanded by the nature of the problems now faced in this field. These facilities will create capabilities for observational research commensurate with these demands, and quite beyond any yet provided. The manpower, the techniques, and the engineering competence for realization of this goal are all in sight, but adequate support must be provided.

SUMMARY OF RECOMMENDATIONS AND COSTS

The cost of the program discussed in Sections III and IV is established in this section. The proposed program as laid out consists of the following items.

Optical Astronomy

1) *Three* large telescopes of the 150-to-200-inch class. The Kitt Peak 150-inch is considered as the first of this group. $60.0 million

2) An engineering study for construction of the largest feasible optical reflector. $ 1.0 million

3) *Four* intermediate-size telescopes of the 60-to-84-inch class. $ 4.0 million

4) *Eight* small modern telescopes of 36-to-48-inch aperture. $ 3.2 million

Total cost of the optical facilities and engineering study is $68.2 million with no operating expense included.

Included in these costs are funds for the initial instrumentation such as spectrographs, photometer, and spectrum scanner with which to start initial operations. Included also is the cost of site-development, land-acquisition, and building for the case of items 1) and 3) above. The details of the cost breakdown and the budget per year to realize the goals are stated in the present section.

Radio Astronomy

1) A very large high-resolution pencil-beam array with low sidelobes to be constructed as a national facility.

Cost of basic dishes.	$30.0 million
Cost of land development with buildings.	$ 4.0 million
Cost of electronics and other auxiliaries.	$ 6.0 million
Total cost	$40.0 million

2) A high-resolution array consisting of about eight antennas to be constructed at the Owens Valley Observatory. $10.0 million

3) Two fully steerable 300-foot paraboloids. $16.0 million

4) Engineering study for the largest possible steerable parabolic antenna. $ 1.0 million

5) Support for existing radio astronomy departments for new small instruments and special, unique problems. $30.0 million

The total support for new radio instruments is then $97.0 million, with no annual support to maintain new facilities included.

Auxiliary Instruments and Automation

1) New auxiliary instruments for both optical and radio. $10.0 million

2) Data-processing instruments and automation of telescopes. $10.0 million

The combined cost of recommended auxiliary instruments and data-processing and automation equipment thus totals $20.0 million.

Annual Operating Support

1) Annual operating support of new optical facilities at a rate of 4 per cent of the value of the facilities completed at any given time. $ 5.3 million

2) Annual operating support of new radio facilities at a rate of 10 per cent of the value of the facilities completed at any given time. $33.6 million

                         Total operating support $38.9 million

The total cost of the entire ten-year program is thus $224.12 million. The detailed breakdown is shown and the budget per year for this program is justified in this section. (See the cost curve in Figure 23, page 86.)

BASIS OF COST ESTIMATES AND PROJECTED SPENDING RATE

Facilities Cost Estimates

Estimating the cost of large research instruments that have not yet been built is admittedly difficult. The Panel is well aware of the fact that the figures submitted in this Report may meet with considerable skepticism. Such doubts are not surprising in view of the number of times that enthusiastic proponents of new research facilities in the physical sciences have seriously underestimated the cost. Astronomical ventures have by no means been immune from this experience.

    Nevertheless the Panel has arrived at a set of cost estimates which it feels it can put forward with reasonable confidence. The principal reason for this confidence is the nature of the recommendations: the major facilities, both radio and optical, are based on designs and components that have already been built, so that neither the feasibility nor the costs are in any great doubt. The decision to recommend facilities of this nature for immediate construction took into consideration both the research requirements—the type of instruments that will bring observational answers to important problems—and the need to get new telescopes into the hands of the under-instrumented astronomical community in the shortest possible time. The recommended construction program should not only yield an optimum return from the investment of available manpower and funds, but should also be subject to minimum uncertainty in the cost estimates.

Radio and optical telescopes larger and more complicated than any yet built, which would involve costs difficult to estimate at present, have not been recommended for construction within the ten-year period; rather they have been reserved for consideration by study groups which will provide not only a thorough-going feasibility analysis, but also detailed cost estimates.

The cost evaluations for the instruments recommended in the coming ten-year period are based on the engineering experience of a member of the Panel who has participated, either directly or as an adviser, in the recent construction of large telescopes, both radio and optical. Through this experience and a continuously updated record of the costs of telescope construction elsewhere, he has assembled the cost survey data summarized in the Appendix to this report. The rapidly growing industrial experience in this highly specialized field has also provided a background of actual costs that is of great assistance in estimating and bidding on new construction projects.

Tables A and B of the Appendix list existing major astronomical facilities, both radio and optical (pages 90 and 96). In Tables C and D of the Appendix are shown the best available data on basic instrument costs for these facilities, in terms of 1963 dollars. The cost data are summarized graphically in Figures 21 and 22, which show cost as a function of size for optical telescopes and for radio astronomy paraboloids.

The costs of optical telescopes fall remarkably close to a mean line showing direct proportionality between cost and collecting area (diameter squared). There is considerably more scatter for the radio astronomy antennas because some of the steerable paraboloids shown in Figure 22 were built for satellite tracking or communications purposes, where operation must be continued under extreme environmental conditions. The mean line, showing cost varying as the 2.5 power of the diameter, passes through points representing dishes built to the tolerances acceptable in radio astronomy, where the rapid and variable motions needed for satellite tracking are not required, and where temporary shutdowns during high winds or icing conditions are not serious.

The estimated total construction costs of the recommended facilities are based on the accumulated data shown in Figures 21 and 22. The adoption of a practical construction schedule then leads to a forecast of the year-

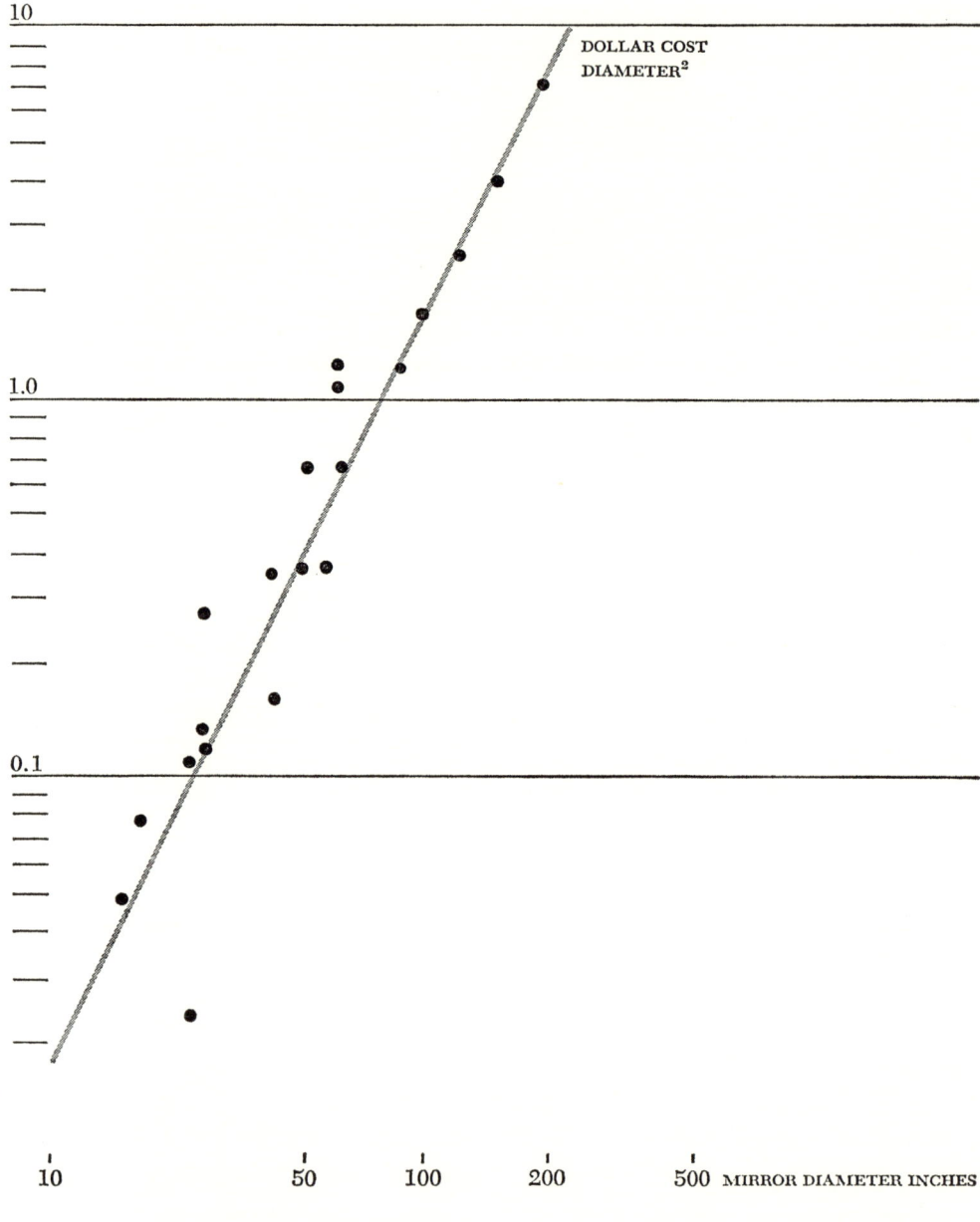

Figure 21
Costs of optical telescopes as a function of aperture, in millions of 1963 dollars. The data are from Table F (p.105, Appendix) and include optics, mounting, and dome. Land costs, site development, and auxiliary instruments are not included.

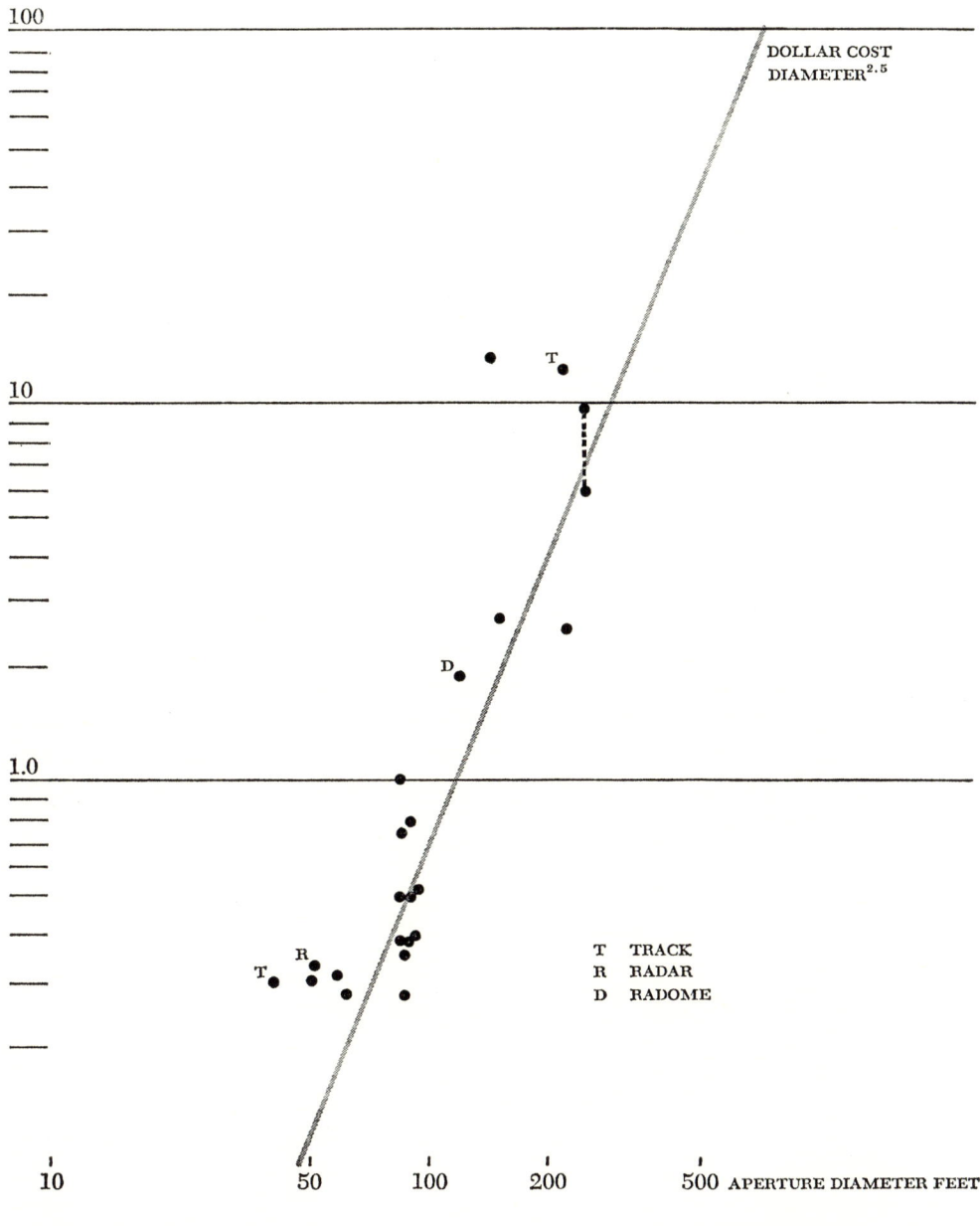

Figure 22
Costs of steerable antennas as a function of diameter, in millions of 1963 dollars, from Table E (p. 104, Appendix). Paraboloids with added construction features not ordinarily needed for radio astronomy are marked with a special symbol. See text, p. 77 for explanation.

to-year funding needed through the ten-year period covered by the present report.

Since the astronomical program proposed involves multiple production of existing types of basic instruments wherever possible, the total facility costs for each size classification can be tabulated in terms of unit cost. Table 3 gives the total cost per unit or total facility with a breakdown taken from basic and auxiliary instrumentation costs of optical telescopes and radio antennas already in operation or now under construction. In the case of large optical telescopes, it is necessary, of course, to make site surveys, to acquire and develop property at new observing sites, and to construct buildings and facilities for supporting activities. For the Northern Hemisphere there can be dependence on large industrial facilities within a reasonable distance of the site chosen. However, a large telescope in the Southern Hemisphere would involve additional expense for the remote site facilities, shipping, labor, and related costs, as noted in Table 3.

The second portion of Table 3 indicates the corresponding cost of facility items for the three types of radio telescope instruments proposed.

The planning, engineering designs, procurement, and erection schedules for large radio and optical facilities must be dovetailed to equalize the load on manufacturing facilities and available technical manpower. The practical fabrication and construction times for the optical telescopes are shown in Table 4, together with the proposed number of units involved. The schedule times are based on recent experience in the construction of similar facilities.

The corresponding estimates for fabrication time for the large radio telescopes and arrays are indicated in the second half of Table 4, along with the corresponding schedules for construction.

Annual Operating Support for New Facilities

Before using the information in Table 3 to prepare a schedule of funding over a ten-year period, it is necessary to inquire what allowance must be made for support of the research programs that will grow up around the new instruments as they are completed. Universities, research institutions, and national centers will be required to assume the added expense of operating these large and complex research tools in a rather short interval. The already serious problem of annual support at all observatories, both radio and optical, will become acute unless there is advance planning and unless funding agencies can anticipate the demand.

TABLE 3   MAJOR ASTRONOMICAL TELESCOPES *Average Cost Per Unit Observatory Facility*

ITEM	FACILITY DESCRIPTION	COSTS OF FACILITY—$ MILLION (1963)				TOTALS
		BASIC[a] TELES.	AUX. INSTRS. ETC.	SITE-DEV. BLDG. & REMOTE	OTHER COST CONTINGENT	AVER. UNIT FACILITY COST
A	*Optical Telescopes*					
1.	36 to 48″ for Univ. Astron. Dept.	$ 0.3			0.1	$ 0.4
2.	60 to 84″ for Good Obs. Univ. Sites	0.8	0.12		0.08	1.0
3.	150 to 200″ for Best Obs. Sites: No. Hemis.	8.5	2.3	5.7	2.0	18.5
	So. Hemis.	8.5	2.3	9.2	3.0	23.0
B	*Radio Telescopes*					
1.	High-Resolution Pencil Beam Array, Multiple Units—Nat'l. Facility (Cost of entire system)	30.0	4.0	4.0	2.0	40.0
2.	Aperture Synthesis Mobile Array Multiple Units of 130′ Steerable at Existing Obs. Site, per unit	1.10	0.10		0.05	1.25
3.	Fully Steerable 300′ Paraboloids at Existing Observatory Sites	7.5	0.2		0.3	8.0

[a] *Basic telescope construction costs taken from Figures 21 and 22 pages 78-79, showing cost vs. aperture for major optical and radio telescopes.*

TABLE 4   CONSTRUCTION-FABRICATION TIME FOR UNIT ASTRONOMICAL FACILITY

	FACILITY DESCRIPTION	CONSTR. TIME PER UNIT (YEARS)	PROPOSED CONSTR. UNITS	SCHEDULES POSSIBLE (YEARS)	NOTE
A	*Optical Telescopes*				
1.	36 to 48″ for Univ. Astron. Dept.	2±	8	Over 1st 8 yrs.	Modern reflectors
2.	60 to 84″ for Univ. Obs. Sites	4	4	2 in 5 yrs. 2 in next 4 yrs.	Urgent early Obs. research
3.	150 to 200″ for Best Obs. Sites: No. Hemis.	8±	2	1 in 8 years 2nd by 10 yrs.	Existing designs
	So. Hemis.	10	1	Spread over 10 yrs.	Site and develop.
4.	Large Telescope Study	4	0	Latter few yrs.	For future recom.
B	*Radio Telescopes*				
1.	High-Resolution Nat'l. Pencil Array	9	1	Continuing	Extendable array
2.	130-ft. Mobile Steerable	1.5±	8	4 in 3 yrs. 4 in next 3 yrs.	Early need; movable parabolic array
3.	300-ft. Steerable Paraboloid	4	2	1 in 4+ yrs. 1 in 6+ yrs.	Polariz. and Spectral studies
4.	Large Telescope Study	4	0	First few yrs.	May affect 300-ft.

A complete analysis of the operating costs of existing observatories is difficult because support comes from many sources and is accounted for in many different ways. Since the impact will be greatest upon those having to operate the largest new facilities, it will be sufficient to use a formula for computing annual support costs based on the experience of the larger research centers already in operation. An examination of the known annual operating costs of the five or six largest observatories in this country shows that the ratio of the annual cost to the 1963 estimated capital value of the facility falls in a remarkably narrow range between 2.5 and 3.5 per cent. In addition, other recent large telescope proposals have also indicated annual operating support ranging from 3.5 to 4.75 per cent of the total proposed facility value. A correlated experience may also be noted: many large university and college campus building programs show annual operating costs for laboratory building and facilities running from 3.5 to 4.5 per cent of the total plant value. It appears adequate, therefore, to recommend that, for the additions to established optical observatories, the allowance for annual operation of newly completed facilities be set at 4 per cent of the construction cost.

On the other hand, experience with large radio telescopes clearly indicates a very different set of annual operating costs, involving a much higher percentage of construction costs; the range is from about 10 per cent to, in some cases, over 28 per cent of the value of the facility. These higher operating costs arise from the special nature of the facilities and the peculiar operating problems of radio observatories. An arbitrary examination of the particular facilities recommended in this report indicates that a 10 per cent formula for annual operation would be justified. This rate is two or three times higher than that for the corresponding optical observatories because: (1) the radio observatories are growing, and operating costs are high on new facilities; (2) advances in electronic techniques make for rapid obsolescence of auxiliary equipment, such as receivers, and frequent replacement is necessary; (3) most radio observatories are much further removed from university centers than are optical observatories, with correspondingly higher travel and operating costs; (4) at radio observatories work is carried on both day and night, with higher costs for double crews; (5) antenna systems cover a much larger property area, with higher road and grounds maintenance costs, and higher communication costs.

It should be emphasized that the percentage figures adopted here for the annual operating ("housekeeping") cost of new facilities cover only the added technical costs such as operating and maintenance personnel, scientific and maintenance supplies, and data-processing and computer charges. They do not include salaries of academic or scientific staff, support of graduate students, or other program-cost items such as scientific libraries. In various institutions the latter costs may be divided in so many different ways between old and new telescopes, between observational and non-observational research, and between teaching and research, that it would be difficult to arrive at a universal formula.

Since the assigned task of the Panel has been to consider the *new* facilities that will be needed in the next ten years, it has not attempted to examine the total problem of the support of astronomical teaching and research in the United States. Thus the figures presented here should not be construed as representing the total government support needed by American astronomy. The problem of annual support is being considered by a panel of the Physics Survey Committee, appointed by the National Academy of Sciences to make a long-range study of physics and its requirements.

According to the estimates of the Physics Survey panel, the total support cost, including small project facilities, is between $10 million and $20 million a year with the present physical plant. Since our recommendations will approximately double the existing facilities and will accommodate nearly twice the number of astronomers by the end of the decade, it may be assumed that the total support cost will also approximately double if the same unit cost per astronomer prevails. Thus, the technical ("housekeeping") costs shown in Table 5 constitute approximately one half of the total additional operating cost needed to support the scientific programs to be carried by the new facilities. Undoubtedly these costs will continue to be divided between normal university budgets and federal grant monies.

Spending Rate

The unit costs for new facilities from Table 3 and the construction schedules from Table 4 are combined in Table 5, and the growth of annual operating costs is computed according to the 4 per cent and 10 per cent formulas adopted in the previous section. This table shows the spending rate for construction of each type of facility and also the accumulated value of all the facilities completed at the end of each year of the program. The latter figure is used for calculation of the corresponding annual operating support that will be needed as the new instruments go into actual research operation.

In addition to the spending for the major facilities and for their operating support as they are completed, the total spending rate must take into account other parts of the over-all recommended program. These costs are

TABLE 5   ANNUAL OPERATING COST OF NEW FACILITIES—$ MILLION
Based on Construction Schedule

	QTY.	FACILITY	COST AT SCHEDULED TIME OF COMPLETION—OF UNIT FACILITIES FOR OPERATION										10-YEAR TOTAL FACILITY COST
			1	2	3	4	5	6	7	8	9	10	
A		Optical											
1.	8	36/48″ Teles.	$0.0	0.4	0.8	0.4	0.4	0.4	0.4	0.4	—	—	$ 3.2
2.	4	60/84″ Teles.	—	—	—	1.0	—	1.0	—	1.0	—	1.0	4.0
3.	3	150/200″ Best Site:											
		No. Hemis.	—	—	—	—	—	—	—	18.5	—	18.5	
		So. Hemis.	—	—	—	—	—	—	—	—	—	23.0	60.0
		Value of year's addition to completed facilities	0.0	0.4	0.8	1.4	0.4	1.4	0.4	19.9	—	42.5	67.2
		Accumulated value of completed facilities	0.0	0.4	1.2	2.6	3.0	4.4	4.8	24.7	24.7	67.2	
		Annual operating support at 4% rate[a]	0.0	0.16	0.048	0.104	0.120	0.176	0.192	0.988	0.988	2.688	5.3
B		Radio											
1.	1	Pencil-Beam Array	0.0	4.0	5.0	5.0	5.0	5.0	5.0	5.0	5.0	1.0	40.0
2.	1	8 Ant. Mobile Array	0.0	—	1.25	2.50	2.50	2.50	1.25	—	—	—	10.0
3.	2	300-ft. Steerable	—	—	—	—	8.0	—	—	—	8.0	—	16.0
		Value of year's addition to completed facilities	0.0	4.0	6.25	7.50	15.50	7.50	6.25	5.0	13.0	1.0	66.0
		Accumulated value of completed facilities	0.0	4.0	10.25	17.25	33.25	40.75	47.00	52.00	65.00	66.00	
		Annual operating support at 10% rate[a]	0.0	0.40	1.025	1.775	3.325	4.075	4.700	5.200	6.500	6.600	33.6
		Total Annual Operating Support, Optical and Radio	0.0	0.416	1.073	1.879	3.445	4.251	4.892	6.188	7.488	9.288	38.9

[a] See text for operation-support-rate formulation.

shown in Table 6; some of the figures already developed in Table 5 are repeated. The study group to consider the largest feasible optical telescope is programmed in the latter years of the decade, not only to give time for the launching of the major new telescopes, but also to make use of the information and expertise developed during the period of their engineering and construction. The work of the proposed radio astronomy study group to consider the largest possible movable paraboloid is scheduled on a somewhat more urgent basis, since its conclusions may influence the construction of the second 300-foot paraboloid that is recommended and could result in its conversion into a larger instrument. Line C of Table 6 includes the provision for auxiliary instrumentation recommended in Section V of the report and also the funds for automation and data-processing, likewise advocated in that Section. The funding for these programs is divided fairly evenly over the years, in the expectation that there will be a great demand for this type of instrumentation in radio astronomy in the first two years, followed by the same type of support for the new optical telescopes as they are completed. Line D of Table 6 lists the annual operating support of research programs using the new instruments, both radio and optical, taken from the schedules shown in Table 5.

The total projected ten-year spending schedule, shown in the final line of Table 6, is displayed graphically in Figure 23. Of the total of $224 million for the ten-year period, the facilities for ground-based optical astronomy amount to $68.2 million and those for radio astronomy to $97 million. The accumulated operating support for the completed facilities at the end of

TABLE 6   PROPOSED 10-YEAR BUDGET—$ MILLION—*Facilities Construction and Operation*

	QTY.	FACILITY	\multicolumn{10}{c}{BUDGET YEARS—FOR SCHEDULED FACILITIES}	10-YEAR TOTAL COSTS
			1	2	3	4	5	6	7	8	9	10	
A		*Optical*											
1.	8	36-48" Teles.—Univ.	$0.2	0.4	0.6	0.6	0.4	0.4	0.4	0.2	—	—	$ 3.2
2.	4	60-84" at Univ. Sites	0.2	0.3	0.6	0.4	0.6	0.4	0.6	0.4	0.4	0.1	4.0
3.	3	150-200" at Best Sites	3.0	6.0	8.0	7.5	7.0	6.5	6.5	7.0	5.0	3.5	60.0
4.	1	Teles. Study Group	—	—	—	—	—	.25	.25	.25	.25	—	1.0
5.	0	New & Replacement Equip.	—	—	—	—	—	—	—	—	—	—	—
		Total Optical	3.4	6.7	9.2	8.5	8.0	7.55	7.75	7.85	5.65	3.6	68.2
B		*Radio*											
1.	1	Pencil-Beam Array	2.0	3.0	4.0	5.0	5.0	5.0	5.0	5.0	4.0	2.0	40.0
2.	1	8 Ant. Mobile Array	1.0	2.0	2.5	2.5	1.5	0.5	—	—	—	—	10.0
3.	2	300-ft. Steerable	1.0	2.0	2.0	3.0	3.0	2.0	2.0	1.0	—	—	16.0
4.	1	Large Ant. Study Group	—	0.25	0.25	0.25	0.25	—	—	—	—	—	1.0
5.	15	Univ. New—Replace.	3.0	3.0	3.0	3.0	3.0	3.0	3.0	3.0	3.0	3.0	30.0
		Total Radio	7.0	10.25	11.75	13.75	12.75	10.50	10.00	9.00	7.00	5.00	97.0
C		Instruments, Data Processing, Automation (Opt. & Radio)	2.0	2.0	2.0	2.0	2.0	2.0	2.0	2.0	2.0	2.0	20.0
D		Annual Oper. Support	—	.416	1.073	1.879	3.445	4.251	4.892	6.188	7.488	9.288	38.9
		Total Proposed	12.400	19.366	24.023	26.129	26.195	24.301	24.642	25.038	22.138	19.888	224.1

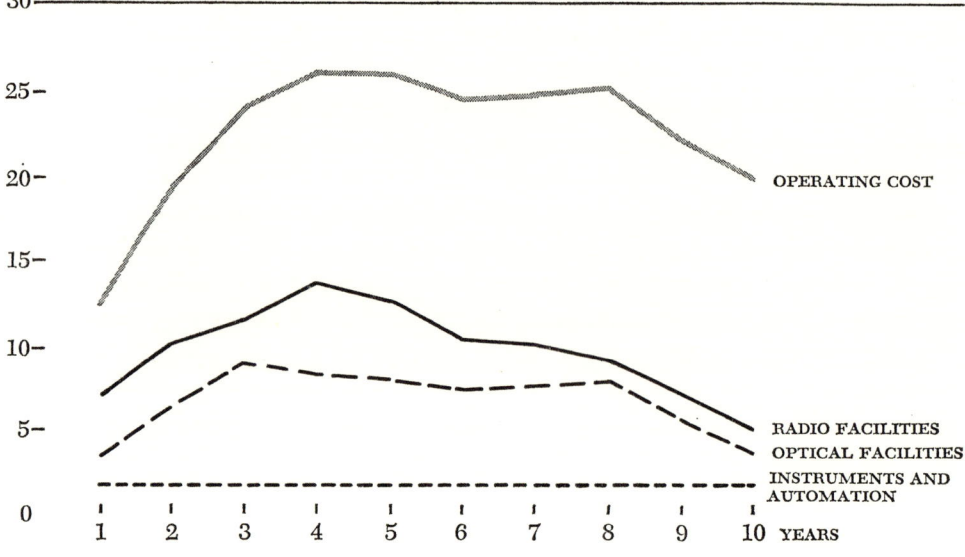
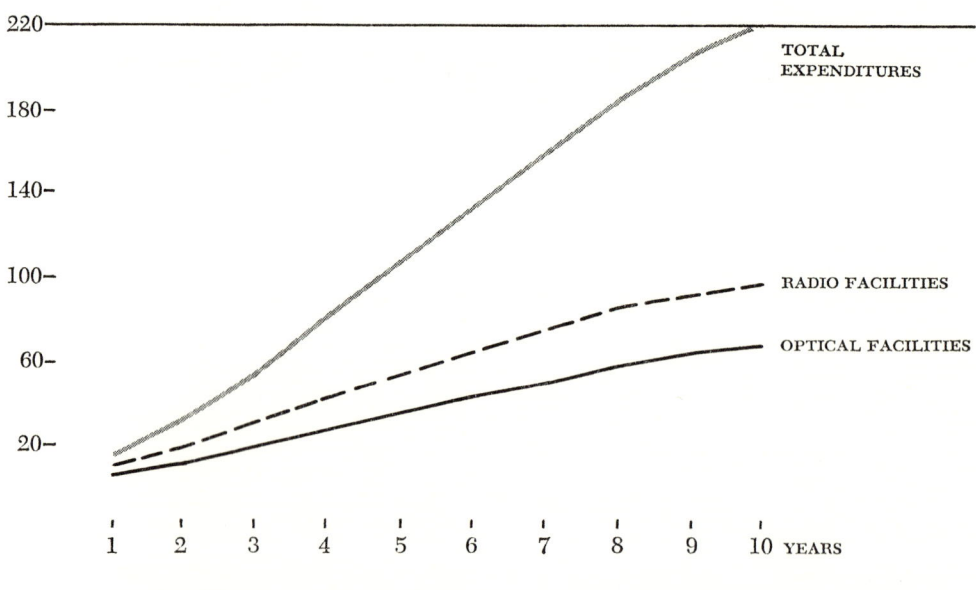

Figure 23
Spending rates in millions of dollars over the 10-year period, including operating costs of completed facilities. The lower panel shows the accumulated expenditures at the end of each year.

ten years amounts to $38.9 million, and the annual support level reaches $9.3 million in the last year of the program. The over-all annual rate of expenditure rises in the first four years to a maximum of about $26 million a year, with a gradual decline to about $20 million a year at the end of the decade.

The decline in the predicted rate toward the end of the decade requires a word of clarification. It arises from the fact that a ten-year program of facilities construction must proceed on the assumption that all the instruments will be completed at the end of the decade. It is, of course, likely, and perhaps almost certain, that, well before the end of the ten-year period, other vitally important facilities now unforeseeable will have appeared on the horizon. Whether these can be built within an annual expenditure rate that is stabilized at the maximum predicted figure in the fourth and fifth years of the current program, or will require a continued growth in spending, cannot now be foretold. There would indeed be reason to question the vitality of American astronomy if the instruments here recommended were found sufficient for many decades, rather than merely for the immediately foreseeable future.

Annual Scientific Support for Existing Facilities

Although it is not a part of the Panel's task to make detailed recommendations on the scale of total annual support, it does wish to record its deep concern over the problem of maintaining a proper balance of support. Without diminishing its emphasis on essential new ground-based facilities, the Panel urges that there not be any diversion of support from or neglect of on-going programs in existing observatories and university departments. It is particularly important, the Panel feels, to maintain a distribution of federal support that will ensure an equitable balance between astronomical effort in national centers and that in university departments.

APPENDIX

This appendix provides background information about existing astronomical facilities and their costs. This material has been used by the Panel in reaching its conclusions and establishing the cost estimates in the text of the report. It includes:

Table A   Major radio telescopes, world-wide, 30 feet or over in size.

Table B   Major optical telescopes, world-wide, 20 inches or greater in aperture, built since 1945.

Table C   Major astronomical facilities, built since 1945 by U. S. institutions with federal financial support.

Table D   Major astronomical facilities built since 1945 by U. S. institutions with state financial support.

Table E   Large radio astronomy parabolic antennas and their cost.

Table F   Large optical telescopes and their cost.

Tables A and B are compiled largely from the *American Ephemeris and Nautical Almanac,* listings maintained by the National Science Foundation, a catalog compiled by B. H. Rule (a panel member), and *Telescopes,* edited by G. P. Kuiper, University of Chicago Press, 1960. The remaining tables have been compiled largely from data supplied by the National Science Foundation and data compiled by B. H. Rule through private communications. Wherever costs are given, the actual cost of an instrument has been corrected to represent the cost to produce the instrument in 1963, using correction factors provided by appraisal-listings services for typical equipment in the United States.

Tables A and B give a good picture of the extent of astronomical facilities at present. From this, a picture can be obtained of the status, relative to the world-wide picture, of American astronomical facilities. The extent of federal and state support can be ascertained from Tables C and D. Tables E and F provide the basis for understanding of the costs of astronomical instruments of all significant sizes.

In Tables E and F, every effort has been made to give an accurate and homogeneous set of costs. This is sometimes difficult, since quoted costs in any given case may or may not include such items as operational support, feasibility studies, site surveys, land procurement and development, auxiliary buildings such as residences and laboratories, and instrumentation for use with the telescope, such as radio receivers, spectrographs, and other auxiliary equipment. The costs of such items have been eliminated wherever possible, although any of them may be necessary in a given project. Thus there may be some inaccuracies in these tables; however, it is felt that any such inaccuracies do not distort the general price picture. The costs shown here are in agreement with those listed in other studies.

The data from Tables E and F have been used to produce Figures 21 and 22, pages 78 and 79. The curves in these figures indicate that the cost of optical telescopes grows as the square of the telescope diameter, and of radio telescopes as the diameter to the 2.5 power. In applying such a simple generalization to obtain an estimate of telescope cost, however, caution must be observed by considering any unusual features of the telescope that may significantly affect costs. Such features may include: 1) extremely large apertures; 2) construction at remote or difficult sites; 3) unusually great dimensional tolerances or stability; 4) a requirement for proper operation and/or protection in severe environments; 5) complex automatic-control or data-acquisition features; 6) a requirement for complex electronic systems.

TABLE A   RADIO ASTRONOMY ANTENNAS—30-foot Size or Larger

LOCATION	OBSERVATORY	SPONSOR	ANTENNA DESCRIPTION Size, Type, Mount, etc.	FREQUENCY	DATE OF OPER.	REMARKS
Arecibo PUERTO RICO	Arecibo Ionospheric Obs.	Cornell Univ. ARPA AFOSR	305m(1000') diameter fixed reflector with 800' arc radius and with steerable correcting feed. Built into natural earth sinkhole.	430 Mc(40-1420 Mc)	1963	
Belmar NEW JERSEY	Evans Signal Laboratory	U.S. Army Elec. Res. & Dev. Lab.	18.3m(60') paraboloid, steerable, alt-az. 15.2m(50') paraboloid, steerable, alt-az.	100-3000 Mc		
Berlin-Adlershof GERMANY	Heinrich Hertz Institute	Deutsche Akademie der Wissenschaften	36m(118') paraboloid, steerable in altitude only. Transit mount.	1500 Mc	1958	
Bethany CONNECTICUT	Yale Univ. Obs.	Yale Univ. NSF	Two 24-element helix arrays, each 2mx40m. Transit, steerable in altitude only. Used as interferometer. Three steerable Yagi arrays 40'x25'.	200-300 Mc 20 Mc		
Big Pine CALIFORNIA	CIT Owens Valley Obs.	Calif. Univ. of Tech.-ONR NSF	Two 27.4m(90') paraboloids. Steerable, equatorial mount. Used as interferometer. 10m(32') paraboloid, steerable, equatorial.	Up to 3 Gc	1958	1956 moved to present site 1958
Bologna ITALY	Univ. of Bologna Astr. Laboratory	Ministry of Pub. Educ.	10m(33') steerable paraboloid. 620mx36m parabolic cylinder E-W axis. 32 cylinders 50mx7m 10m apart on N-S axis. Adjustable in elevation transit instrument.	327 Mc 408 Mc		Under construction.
Boulder COLORADO	High Altitude Obs.	AFCRL NSF	Two 24.4x13.8m (80'x46') trihedral steerable corner reflectors, alt-az.	15-60 Mc	1955	
Boulder COLORADO	Boulder Labs.	Nat'l Bureau Standards	Two 26m(85') paraboloids, E-W separation. 66m; 18.3 diameter, alt-az, paraboloid 3400' distant. Two 18.3m(60') paraboloids, alt-az, interferometer-fixed spacing approximately 900 feet.	900-1100 Mc 16-75 Mc	1959	
Burakan USSR	Astro. Obs.		Four cylindrical paraboloids, fixed. 10m(32.8') paraboloid.			
Cambridge ENGLAND	Mullard Radio Astro. Obs.	Dept. of Sci. & Ind. Res.	442x19.8m(1450x65') parabolic cylinder, steerable in altitude only. Synthesized interferometer. 1000x12.2m(3300x40') corner reflector, steerable in altitude only. Synthesized cross. Two 7.5m(24.6') paraboloid, equatorial mount.	178 Mc 38 Mc		

TABLE A (cont'd)

LOCATION	OBSERVATORY	SPONSOR	ANTENNA DESCRIPTION Size, Type, Mount, etc.	FREQUENCY	DATE OF OPER.	REMARKS
			Three 18.3m(60') equatorial paraboloid, synthesized 1500m(5000') circular aperture.	400-1420 Mc	1964	
Clark Lake CALIFORNIA	Clark Lake Radio Obs.	Univ. of Maryland NSF	Dipole array 2 miles E-W, 1 mile N-S.	26 Mc	1961	
College ALASKA	USAF, Geophys. Institute	Univ. of Alaska NSF	Two 8.53m(28') steerable, polarmounted paraboloid providing interferometer. 18.6m(61') diameter steerable paraboloid.	223 Mc and 456 Mc simul. 398 Mc		
Crimea USSR (Simeis)	Crimean Astro. Obs.	Lebedev Phys. Institute (Acad. Sci. USSR)	18x8m(59x26.2') cylindrical paraboloid, steerable, alt-az. 19m(62.8') paraboloid, steerable, alt-az. Two 31m(101') fixed, transit zinc-painted on concrete, used as interferometer with 800m E-W baseline. 72m(236') steerable, paraboloid, under construction. No other information.	to 1.4 Gc		
Danville ILLINOIS	Univ. of Illinois Vermilion River Obs.	Univ. of Illinois ONR AF	183x122m(600x400')x18.5m deep. Fixed aperture, parabolic cylinder scooped out of earth. 9m(28') paraboloid, alt-az mount.	611 Mc 100-1000 Mc	1962 1960	
Delaware OHIO	Perkins Obs. Radio Teles.	Ohio State U. NSF AFCRL	111x213m(360x70') standing paraboloid, fixed (tiltable plane reflector). With plane reflector 111x30.5m(260x100'). 12.2m(40') steerable paraboloid, equatorial mount.	40 Mc- 2000 Mc 915 Mc	1962 1959	
Dexter MICHIGAN	Obs. Univ. of Michigan	Univ. of Michigan ONR	26m(85') paraboloid, equatorial mount. 9m(28') paraboloid, equatorial mount.	1-16 Gc 100-4000 Mc	1959	
Dwingeloo NETHERLANDS	Neth. Found. Radio Astro. Obs.	Leiden Univ. and Neth. Org. for Pure Res.	25m(83') paraboloid, steerable, alt-az.	400-600- 1420 Mc	1955	
Fairbanks ALASKA	Gilmore Creek Acquisition Facility	NASA	25.9m(85') steerable paraboloid, X-Y mount.	136 Mc 400 Mc 1700 Mc		
Florence ITALY	Arcetri Astrophysical Obs.	Univ. of Florence	10m(33') steerable paraboloid cassagrain type.	10-40 Gc	1964	Nearly completed.
Fort Davis TEXAS	Harvard Radio Astr. Station	AFCRL NSF	26m(85') steerable paraboloid, equatorial mount. 8.53m(28') steerable paraboloid, equatorial mount.	to 10 Gc to 4 Gc	1961 1956	

TABLE A (cont'd)

LOCATION	OBSERVATORY	SPONSOR	ANTENNA DESCRIPTION Size, Type, Mount, etc.	FREQUENCY	DATE OF OPER.	REMARKS
Gainesville FLORIDA	Univ. of Florida Radio Obs.	ONR NSF	Two 12.2x12.2m(40x40') corner reflector. Transit mount.	13-30 Mc		
Goldstone CALIFORNIA	NASA Deep Space Inst.	JPL-NASA	25.9m(85') steerable parabolic dish, alt-az.	2390 Mc	1958	
			25.9m(85') steerable paraboloid, equator-offset.	960 Mc	1958	
			9.2m(30') diameter steerable, alt-az. Also 25.9m(85') dishes in Woomera, Australia, and South Africa, both equatorial mounts.	3 cm	1963	
Green Bank WEST VIRGINIA	Nat'l Radio Astr. Obs.	AUI NSF	25.9m(85') equatorial, pedestal, steerable paraboloid, fixed base.	400-10,000 Mc	1959	
			25.9m(85') equatorial steerable paraboloid, movable base 5000' to 9000' base line forms interferometer with fixed paraboloid.	400-10,000 Mc	1964	
			91.5m(300')paraboloid, transit mount.	1420 Mc	1962	
			42.7m(140') steerable paraboloid, equatorial mount.	to 15 Gc	1964 Under const.	
			12.2m(40') paraboloid, meridian transit.	750 & 1400 Mc		
			9.2m(30') paraboloid, alt-az mount.	to 1427 Mc		
			Standard gain horn-86.5m long, collecting area 10 square meters.	600-1450 Mc		
Hamilton MASSACHUSETTS	Sagamore Hill Radio Obs.	AFCRL	25.6m(84') equatorial mount steerable paraboloid.	to 3 Gc	1958	
			45.8m(150') alt-az, steerable paraboloid.	to 1.5 Gc	1963	
Harvard MASSACHUSETTS	Agassiz Station Harvard College Obs.	Harvard NSF	18.3m(60') steerable paraboloid equatorial mount.	1420 Mc 1-2 Gc	1956	
Hat Creek CALIFORNIA	Univ. of Calif. Radio Obs.	Univ. of California ONR	26m(85') steerable paraboloid, polar mount (equatorial pedestal).	1-10 Gc	1962	
			10.1m(400') steerable, equatorial.	8000 Mc	1960	
Havana ILLINOIS		Nat'l Bur. of Standards	116x140m (broadside array of 32x32.5 dipoles).	41 Mc	1958	
Hoskinstown AUSTRALIA	Molonglo River Observatory	Univ. of Sydney NSF	Large mills cross E-W parabolic cylinder 5100' long variable declination by tilting. N-S parabolic cylinder 5100' long variable declination by phase adjustment.	111-408 Mc		Under const. 1965
Humain-Rochefort BELGIUM	Radio Obs.	Royal Obs. of Belgium	Array of 48 dishes 4m in dia., 32 in E-W line, 16 in N-S.	408 Mc		Under const.
Lake Traverse ONTARIO, CANADA	Algonquin Radio Obs.	Nat'l Res. Council	10m(33') paraboloid, equatorial mount.	to 16 Gc	1963	
			45.8m(150') steerable paraboloid, equatorial.	300-2000 Mc		Under const.

TABLE A *(cont'd)*

LOCATION	OBSERVATORY	SPONSOR	ANTENNA DESCRIPTION Size, Type, Mount, etc.	FREQUENCY	DATE OF OPER.	REMARKS
			185m linear array (compound interferometer).	3000 Mc		1951—with additions.
LaPlata ARGENTINA	Radio Obs.	Argentine Nat. Research Council Carnegie Inst. NSF	30m paraboloid limited steerability.	1420 Mc		Under const.
Leningrad USSR	Pulkovo Obs.	Acad. Sci. USSR	16m(52.5') fixed paraboloid. 120x3m(394x10') parabolic sector (adjustable in altitude only). Two 12m(39.4') paraboloids, transit mount. Used as interferometer with parabolic sector.	300 Mc 1000-3000 Mc 178 Mc	1958 1957	
Leningrad (KISLOVOKSK, N. CAUCASUS, USSR)	Pulkovo Obs.	Acad. Sci. USSR	Two 10x2m(33x7') cylindrical paraboloids, transit mount.	178 Mc		
Lima PERU	Jicamara Radio Obs.	NBS and Inst. Geophys. Lima	288x288m(995x995') broadside array.	50 Mc	1962	
Macclesfield ENGLAND	Jodrell Bank Exp. Station	Nuffield Found. Dept. of Sci. and Ind. Res. Univ. of Manchester ONR	76.2(250') steerable paraboloid, alt-az. 9.15m(30') steerable paraboloid, alt-az. 15.5m(50') paraboloid, equatorial mount. 24.4x36.6m(80x120') elliptical paraboloid, alt-az mount.	20 Mc- 1420 Mc 1420 Mc to 10 Gc to 3 Gc	1957 1963 1964	
Maipu, Santiago CHILE	Univ. of Chile Maipu Radio Astro. Obs.	Univ. of Chile Univ. of Florida NSF	12.2x12.2m(40x40') corner reflector, transit mount.	13-30 Mc	1960	
Malvern WORCESTERSHIRE ENGLAND	Royal Radar Establishment	Ministry of Aviation Ministry of Supply	13.7m(45') steerable paraboloid, alt-az. Two 25m(82') diameter steerable paraboloid, alt-az.	3000 Mc to 3000 Mc	 1960	
Maryland Point CHARLES' COUNTY MARYLAND	Maryland Pt. Obs.	NRL	25.6m(84'), steerable, equatorial mount. 26m(85') steerable equatorial.	400-3000 Mc	1957 Under const.	
Nançay FRANCE	Meudon Obs.	Obs. de Paris	Eight 10m(32.8') & thirty-two 5m (16.4') paraboloids, steerable in altitude only, transit mount. Used in interferometer to synthesize 770m aperture.	169 Mc	1955	

TABLE A (cont'd)

LOCATION	OBSERVATORY	SPONSOR	ANTENNA DESCRIPTION Size, Type, Mount, etc.	FREQUENCY	DATE OF OPER. REMARKS
			300x35m(1000x115') standing spherical with plane reflector 200x40m(650'x131') Fixed (tiltable plane reflector).	1420 Mc 2300 Mc	1964 Under const.
Nederhorst den Berg NETHERLANDS	Ned. den Berg Obs.	Neth. Postal and Telecom. Service	7.5m(24.6') steerable paraboloid, alt-az. 10m(32.8') steerable paraboloid, alt-az.	200 Mc 200 Mc	
Onsala SWEDEN (GOTHENBERG)	Onsala Radio Wave Prop. Obs.	Chalmers Univ. of Tech.	Two 7.5m(24.6') steerable paraboloid, equatorial. 18m(60') steerable paraboloid, equatorial. Two broadside arrays.	190 Mc 1420 Mc 3000 Mc 25 Mc	
Parkes, N.S.W. AUSTRALIA	CSIRO Radiophysics Lab.	CSIRO	64m(210') steerable paraboloid, alt-az. 18.2m(60') steerable alt-az paraboloid movable can be used as an interferometer.	600-2000 Mc 1420 Mc	1961 1962
Penticton BRITISH COLUMBIA (WHITE LAKE STA.)	Dominion Rad. Astro. Obs.	Dept. of Mines and Tech.	25.6m(84') steerable paraboloid, equatorial. Large (2000'), low-frequency T-shaped interferometer.	1420 Mc 26 Mc	1959 1964 Under const.
Potsdam GERMANY	Potsdam Astr. Obs.	Deutsch Akad. du Wissenshft.	10.5m(34.4') steerable paraboloid, equatorial mount.	to 3Gc	
Rosman NORTH CAROLINA		NASA	25.9m(85') steerable paraboloid, X-Y mount.	136 Mc 400 Mc 1700 Mc	
Saint-Michel FRANCE	Haute-Provence Obs.	Ctr. Nacional de la Recherche Scientifique	Two 32x60m(105x197') parabolic cyl., used as interferometer.	300 Mc	
San Diego CALIFORNIA	Naval Elect. Laboratory	NEL	18.3m(60') paraboloid, alt-az mount.	to 10 Gc	
Serpukhov (near Moscow) USSR	Serpukhov Radiophys. Sta.	Lebedev Phys. Institute	22m(72') paraboloid, steerable, alt-az. Two 1kmx40m(328x131') parabolic cylinder steerable in altitude only, used as Mills Cross to synthesize 500m aperture at 3m.	to 37 Gc 50 Mc-150 Mc	1959 1963+
So. Gloucester ONTARIO CANADA	Goth Hill Obs.	Nat'l Res. Council	45x0.45m(151x1.51') transit mount, steerable about E-W axis.	2700 Mc 3000 Mc	
Stanford CALIFORNIA	Stanford U. Radioscience Lab.	Stanford Univ. AFOSR NSF	110m(350') cross principally for solar observation. Array—3m(10') dishes (16) parabolic, steerable, alt-az, in a row 375' long bisected at a right angle by a similar row. Equal to a 375' paraboloid.	3000 Mc 3300 Mc	1959

TABLE A (cont'd)

LOCATION	OBSERVATORY	SPONSOR	ANTENNA DESCRIPTION Size, Type, Mount, etc.	FREQUENCY	DATE OF OPER.	REMARKS
(BOSEMAN, MONTANA)	Stanford Res. Institute	AFCRL Rome Air Dev. Ctr.	2 additional dishes form a compound inteferometer. Four 9.2m(30') paraboloid, equatorial mount. 45.7m(150') steerable paraboloid, alt-az mount. 18.6m(61') steerable paraboloid, alt-az.	3000 Mc	1962+	
State College PENNSYLVANIA	Radio Obs.	Penn State Univ.	10m(30') steerable equatorial mount. Array of dipoles 50'x30'.	980-3000 Mc 74 Mc	1962 1964	
Stockert GERMANY	Bonn Univ. Obs.	Bonn. Univ.	25m(83') steerable paraboloid, alt-az.	to 3 Gc	1956	
Sugar Grove WEST VIRGINIA	Naval Radio Research Sta.	U.S. Navy (NRL)	18m(60') steerable paraboloid, equatorial.	to 10 Gc	1961	
Sydney AUSTRALIA (FLEURS)	Fleurs Field Station	Univ. of Sydney	1110m(3500') Mills Cross. 461.5m(1500') Mills Cross. 381m(1240') Cross. 32x32 elements-19' parab., equatorial mount.	20 Mc 85 Mc 1500 Mc	1957 1952 1957	
(NARRA BRI)	CSIRO Radiophysics Lab.	CSIRO	Radio heliograph 96 steerable paraboloids 13m(42') in dia. in a circular array 3km in dia.	80-110 Mc		Under const.
(POTTS HILL)			11m(36') paraboloid, steerable in altitude only. Transit mount. Two 2000mx1m corner reflector, separation 600m.	600-1420 Mc 400 Mc	1958	
Tokyo JAPAN		Univ. of Tokyo	10m(32.8') paraboloid, equatorial mount.	200 Mc		
Washington, D.C.		Carnegie Institution	40m(120') equatorial paraboloid. 461.5m(1500') Mills Cross. 923m(3000') linear array of corner reflector. 18.3m(60') equatorial paraboloid.	to 1.4 Gc 21 Mc 87 Mc to 16 Gc	1964 1954 1959 1959	
		NRL	15.5m(50') steerable, high-gain parabolic reflector, alt-az (fork).	25 kmc	1951	
Westford MASSACHUSETTS	Haystack Hill Millstone Hill	Lincoln Laboratory MIT ARDC	36.6m(120') steerable paraboloid, alt-az. 25.6m(84') steerable paraboloid, polar or equatorial mount.	to 10 Gc 400 Mc 1200 Mc	1956	Under const.
Zimenki USSR	Zimenki Radio-Astronomical Station	Gorki Physio-Tech. Res. Inst.	Two 15.2m(50') paraboloids.			Planned

TABLE B   MAJOR ASTRONOMICAL OPTICAL TELESCOPES Since 1945

Cass = Cassegrain; Greg = Gregorian; IR = infrared; Mak = Maksutov (meniscus type) corrector; Nas = Nasmyth; Newt = Newtonian; Refl = reflector; Refr = refractor; Schm = Schmidt corrector lens; Vis = visual. For corrector-type telescopes, first line applies to aperture and optical material of corrector; second line to primary mirror.

LOCATION	OBSERVATORY	SPONSOR	ELEV. (FT)	TELES. TYPE	APERTURE (INCHES)	OPTICS (TYPE)	FOCUS	F/	DATE OF OPER.	REMARKS
Abastumani Georgia USSR	Astrophysical Obs.	Astrophys. Obs.	5250	Refl. (Mak)	28 38	Glass Glass	Prime Cass	3 14	1956	
Alfeite PORTUGAL	Lisbon Obs.	Lisbon Obs.	131	Refl.	20	Glass	Newt Cass	6 18	1950	
Alma-Ata USSR	Astrophysical Institute	Astrophys. Inst.	4750	Refl. Refl. (Mak)	20 20 26.5	Glass Glass Glass	Cass Prime	24 2.4	1948 1950	
Berkeley CALIF.	Leuschner Obs.	U. of Calif.	300	Refl.	20	Pyrex	Newt Cass	4 16	1956	
Berlin GERMANY	Sternwarte Berlin-Badelsberg		270	Refl. Refl.	28 21	Glass Glass	Cass Cass	22 20	1957 1960	
Bern SWITZERLAND	Sternwarte Zimmerwald der Universität Bern		2952	Refl.	24	Glass	Cass	25	1959	
Bloemfontein O.F.S.	Boyden Sta.	Harvard	4549	Baker-Schm.	32 36	Glass Glass	Prime	3.7	1950	
Brno CZECH.	Univ. Obs.	Masaryk U.	909	Refl.	24	Glass	Newt	4.5	1954	
Burakan Armenia USSR	Burakan Astr. Obs.		4854	Schm.	21 21	Glass Pyrex	Prime	3.4	1954	
Cambridge ENGLAND	Univ. Obs.	Cambridge U.	82	Refl.	36	Pyrex	Prime Coudé Coudé	4.5 18 30	1955	
Canberra AUSTRALIA	Mt. Stromlo Obs.	Australian National Observatory	265	Refl.	74	Pyrex	Newt Cass Coudé	5 18 31	1955	
				Refl. Refl.	50 40	Pyrex Pyrex	Greg Cass Coudé	18 8 40	1954 1964	At Siding Spring Sta.
				Refl.	26	Pyrex	Cass	12	1959	At Siding Spring Sta.
				Refr.	26	Glass		16.6	1953	
		Uppsala Obs.		Schm.	20 26	Glass Pyrex	Prime	3.5	1956	

TABLE B (cont'd)

LOCATION	OBSERVATORY	SPONSOR	ELEV. (FT)	TELES. TYPE	OPTICS APERTURE (INCHES)	OPTICS (TYPE)	FOCUS	F/	DATE OF OPER.	REMARKS
Cape of Good Hope SO. AFRICA	Royal Obs.		26	Refl.	40	Pyrex	Prime Cass	4.5 20	1961	
Castel Gandolfo ITALY	Vatican Obs.		1470	Schm.	25 38.5			3.8	1959	
Charlottesville VIRGINIA	Fan Mtn. Obs. Station	Univ. of Va.	1818	Refl.	32	Pyrex	Cass Cass	16 32	1964	
Cleveland OHIO	Warner and Swasey Obs.	Case Inst.	820	Refl.	36	Glass	Cass	14.4	1957	
College Park MARYLAND	Univ. of Md. Astron. Obs.	Univ. of Md.	190	Refl.	20	Pyrex	Cass	15	1964	
Copenhagen DENMARK	Univ. Obs.	U. of Copen.	298	Refl.	20	Pyrex	Cass	14	1958	At Brorfelde Sta.
Crimea (Nauchny) USSR	Crimean Astr. Obs.		1870	Refl.	104	Pyrex	Prime Cass Coudé Nas	3.8 16.4 40 15.7	1960	
				Refl.	48	Glass	Cass	20	1952	
				Refl.	20	Pyrex	Coudé	13	1950	
				Refl. (Mak)	25.2	Glass	Cass	1.4	1951	
Crimea USSR	Sternberg Astronomical Inst. (Southern Sta.)		1968	Refl. (Mak)	20 28	Glass Glass	Prime	4	1958	
				Refl.	50	Glass	Prime Newt Cass	4 4 17	1960	
Delaware OHIO	Perkins Obs.	Ohio State	880	Refl.	32	Pyrex	Newt Cass	4.7 16.5	1958	
Dublin EIRE	Dunsink Obs.		282	Refl.	28	Glass	Coudé	4.3	1957	
Elizabethville CONGO	IRSAC Obs.		4920	Refl.	38.5	Pyrex	Prime Cass Coudé	2 10 10	1960	
				Schm.	26.3 38.5	Quartz Pyrex	Prime		1960	
Flagstaff ARIZ.	Atmos. Res. Obs.	Ariz. State	6900	Refl.	24	Pyrex	Newt	4.5	1953	
Flagstaff ARIZ.	U.S. Naval Obs.	U.S. Navy	7580	Refl.	40	Glass	Cass	6.8	1955	
				Refl.	61	Glass Quartz	Cass	10	1963	Astrometric

TABLE B (cont'd)

LOCATION	OBSERVATORY	SPONSOR	ELEV. (FT)	TELES. TYPE	OPTICS APERTURE (INCHES)	OPTICS (TYPE)	FOCUS	F/	DATE OF OPER.	REMARKS
Flagstaff ARIZ.	Lowell Obs.		7250	Refl. Refl.	20.8 24	Pyrex Pyrex	Cass Cass Cass Cass	16 16 32 104	1953 1960	
	Perkins Obs.	Ohio State		Refl.	69	Glass	Newt Cass		1932, 1962	
Fort Davis TEXAS	McDonald Obs.	U. of Texas U. of Chi.	6825	Refl.	36	Pyrex	Cass	13.6	1957	
Hamburg GERMANY	Hamburg-Bergedorf Sternwarte		131	Schm.	32 48	Glass Glass		3	1955	
Helwan EGYPT	Helwan Obs.		377	Refl.	74	Glass	Newt Cass Coudé	4.9 18 28.9	1960	
Herstmonceux ENGLAND	Royal Greenwich Obs.		152	Refl.	20	Glass	Cass	16	1957	
Hyderabad INDIA	Nizamiah Obs.	Osmania U.	1820	Refl.	48	Pyrex	Newt Cass Coudé	4 15 30	1962	
Jena GERMANY	Univ.-Sternwarte Astro Inst.		1115	Refl. Refl.	20 36	Glass Glass	Newt Cass Cass	5 20 15	1958 1960	
Kiev USSR	Ukr. SSR Acad. Sci.		492	Refl.	28	Glass	Prime Newt Cass	4.5 4.5 15	1959	
Kyoto JAPAN	Kwasan Obs.	Kyoto U.	768	Refl.	24	Pyrex	Newt Cass	5.5 20	1960	
L'Aquila ITALY	Obs. di Roma		7216	Schm.	26 37	Glass Pyrex	Prime	3	1959	
La Serena CHILE	Cerro Tololo Inter-Amer. Obs.	AURA		Refl. Refl.	60 36				Proposed Proposed	
Lausanne SWITZERLAND	Obs. Univ.		1952	Refl.	25	Glass	Newt Cass	3.7 24	1948	
Lembang, Java INDONESIA	Bosscha Obs.		4264	Schm.	20 28	Glass Pyrex	Prime	2.5	1958	
Liège (Cointe-Sclessin) BELGIUM	Univ. Obs.	University	417	Schm.	24	Glass	Prime Cass Coudé	3 3.75 13	1957	
Louisville KY.	Star Lane Obs.	U. of Louisville	469	Refl.	20.3	Pyrex	Newt Cass	5	1956	

TABLE B (cont'd)

LOCATION	OBSERVATORY	SPONSOR	ELEV. (FT)	TELES. TYPE	OPTICS APERTURE (INCHES)	OPTICS (TYPE)	FOCUS	F/	DATE OF OPER.	REMARKS
Madison WIS.	Washburn Obs.	U. of Wis.	1190	Refl.	36	Pyrex	Cass	13.7	1958	
Merate, Como ITALY	Obs. Astron.		1066	Refl.	50	Glass	Newt Cass	5	1960	
Meudon FRANCE	Obs. de Paris		531	Refl.	24	Prime	Cass	12	1949	
Moscow USSR	Sternberg Astr. Inst.		623	Refl.	28	Glass	Prime Newt Cass	4.5 4.5 15	1957	
Mt. Hamilton CALIF.	Lick Obs.	U. of Calif.	4208	Refl. Refl. Refl.	120 22 24	Pyrex Glass Pyrex	Prime Coudé Cass Cass	5 11 18	1959 1956 1964	
Mt. Wilson CALIF.	Mt. Wilson Obs.	Carnegie Inst.	5720	Refl.IR Refl.IR	20 24	Pyrex Glass	Cass Cass	16	1962 1963	For use at White Mtn.
Nashville TENN.	Dyer Obs.	Vanderbilt Univ.	1131	Refl.	24 24	Pyrex Glass	Newt Newt Cass	4.5 3.4 16	1953	
Ondrejov CZECH.	Ondrejov Obs.		1731	Refl. (Mak)	25	Glass	Prime	1.4	1959	
Palomar Mtn. CALIF.	Palomar Mtn. Obs.	Cal Tech Carnegie	5600	Refl. Schm. Refl.	200 48 72 20	Pyrex Glass Pyrex Pyrex	Prime Cass Coudé Prime Cass	3.3 16 30 2.5 12.7	1948 1948 1951	
Philadelphia PA.	Flower and Cook	U. of Pa.	508	Refl.	28	Pyrex	Newt Cass Prime	5 15 5	1956	
Portage Lake MICH.	Portage Lake Obs.	U. of Mich.	1051	Refl. Schm.	24 24 36	Pyrex Pyrex Glass	Cass Prime Newt	25 50 Inf 3.5 3.5	1958 1950	
Potsdam GERMANY	Astro. Phys.		351	Schm. Refl.	20 27 28	Glass Glass Glass	Prime Cass	3.4 32	1952 1957	
Pretoria SO. AFRICA	Radcliffe Obs.		5060	Refl.	74	Pyrex	Newt Cass Coudé	4.8 18 28	1948	

TABLE B *(cont'd)*

LOCATION	OBSERVATORY	SPONSOR	ELEV. (FT)	TELES. TYPE	OPTICS APERTURE (INCHES)	OPTICS (TYPE)	FOCUS	F/	DATE OF OPER.	REMARKS
Provo UTAH	*Brigham Young Univ.*		4725	*Refl.*	24	Pyrex	Prime Newt Cass	3 4 15	1959	
Pulkovo USSR	*Astron. Obs. Acad. Sci.*	Acad. Sci.	246	*Refl.* *Vis Refr.* *Refl. (Mak)*	20 26 27.5	Glass Glass Metal	Coudé Prime Cass Coudé	13.5 16 3 12 29	1951 1957 1960	
Saint Michel FRANCE	*Obs. de Haute Provence*		1901	*Refl.* *Refl.*	77 24	Glass Glass	Newt Cass Coudé Cass	5 15 30 16	1958 1959	
Santiago CHILE	*Nat'l Obs.*	U. Chile	2819	*Refr.*	24	Glass		18.2	1956	
Simeis USSR	*Crimean Obs.*		1146	*Refl. (Mak)*	25.5	Glass	Prime	1.4	1952	
Saltsjöbaden SWEDEN	*Stockholm Obs.*		180	*Schm.*	26 40	Glass Pyrex	Prime	4.6	1960	
Thuringen GERMANY	*Obs. of Ger. Academy*		1081	*Schm.*	54 80	Glass Glass	Prime Cass Coudé	3 10 45	1960	
Tokyo JAPAN	*Tokyo Astr. Obs.*		193 1214 	*Refl.* *Refl.* *Refl.*	36 74 36	Pyrex Pyrex Pyrex	Prime Cass Newt Cass Coudé Cass	5 18 4.9 18 29 13	1961 1960 1960	Mitaka Sta. Okayama Sta.
Tonantzintla MEXICO	*Tonantizintla Obs.*	U. of Mex.	7180	*Schm.*	26 32			3.2	1948	
Tucson ARIZ.	*Kitt Peak Nat'l Obs.*	AURA	6850	*Refl.* *Refl.*	36 84	Pyrex Pyrex	Cass Cass Coudé	13.5 8 32	1961 1964	
Tucson ARIZ.	*Catalina Station*	U. of Ariz.	8390	*Refl.* *Refl.* *Refl.*	21.5 29 60	Pyrex Pyrex Pyrex	Cass Cass Cass	16 16 16	1962 1962 1964	
Uccle BELGIUM	*Royal Obs.*		344	*Schm.*	33 46	Glass Quartz	Prime Cass	2.5 10	1958	
Uppsala SWEDEN	*Uppsala Obs.*		66	*Schm.*	40 54	Glass Pyrex	Prime	3	1962	

TABLE B (cont'd)

LOCATION	OBSERVATORY	SPONSOR	ELEV. (FT)	TELES. TYPE	OPTICS APERTURE (INCHES)	OPTICS (TYPE)	FOCUS	F/	DATE OF OPER.	REMARKS
Victoria, B.C. CANADA	Dominion Obs.		750	Refl.	48	Pyrex	Prime Cass Coudé	4 18 30	1961	
Williams Bay WISCONSIN	Yerkes Obs.	Univ. of Chicago	1100	Refl.	24	Pyrex	Cass		1964	Tube Rotatable for Polarization Studies

Compiled from American Ephemeris and Various Listings by B. H. Rule, Revised March 1964

101

TABLE C   MAJOR FEDERALLY FUNDED ASTRONOMICAL FACILITIES CONSTRUCTED SINCE 1945

OBSERVATORY	SPONSOR	FUNDING AGENT	FACILITY DESCRIPTION				INSTRUMENT COST ONLY AT 1963 PRICE LEVEL— $ THOUSANDS
			SIZE	TYPE	MOUNT	FOR	
Optical Observatory Facilities							
1. Cerro Tololo Inter-Amer. Obs.	AURA	AF-NSF	60" 36"	Cas/cou Cass	Off-Axis Off-Axis	Astro Astro	$ 1,050 250
2. Kitt Pk Nat'l Obs.	AURA	NSF	16" 36" 84" 60" 36" & 50"	Cass Cass Cass/Coudé Solar Cass Remote (Const.)	Off-axis Off-axis Fork Fork	Astro Astro Astro Solar	55 275 2,500 3,500 2,500
							$10,130
3. Sacramento Peak Obs.	Harvard	USAF	4½" 6", 16"	Refr.		Solar Corona- graphs	4,000
4. Climax Obs.	U. Colo.	ONR-AF	10½", 3"	Refr.	Camera	Flare-Patrol	1,500
5. U.S.N. Flagstaff	U.S.N.	USN	60"	Cass	Fork	Astrometric	1,200
					OPTICAL TOTALS		$16,830
Radio Observatory Facilities							
1. National Radio Astron. Obs.	AUI	NSF	85' 140' 300' 13x17'	Parab. Parab. Parab. Horn	Equator. Equator. Merid. Tr.	R. Astro (Const.) Transit Calib.	$ 375 13,500 900 75
							$14,850
2. Owens Valley Obs.	CIT	ONR	(2)90'	Mob. Parab.	Equator.	Interfer.	$ 970
3. Univ. Mich. Obs.	U.M.	ONR	85'	Parab.	Equator.	R. Astro.	375
4. Harvard Coll. Obs.	Harvard	NSF	60' 24'	Parab. Parab.	Equator. Equator.	R. Astro. R. Astro.	110 95
5. Hat Creek Obs.	U.C.	ONR	85' 33'	Parab. Parab.	Equator. Equator.	R. Astro. R. Astro.	350 45
6. Ill. Radio Obs.	U. Ill.	ONR	600x400'	Fixed earth parab. cyl.		Transit	300
7. Stanford	S.U.	A.F.	375' (32)10'	Cross Array Parab.	Equator.	Solar	440
	S.U.	A.F.	(2)30'	Parab.	Equator.	Interfer.	60
	S.U./SRI	A.F.	150'	Parab.	Alt-Az	Radar	350

TABLE C (cont'd)

OBSERVATORY	SPONSOR	FUNDING AGENT	FACILITY DESCRIPTION SIZE	TYPE	MOUNT	FOR	INSTRUMENT COST ONLY AT 1963 PRICE LEVEL— $ THOUSANDS
8. Ohio State	Ohio S.	NSF	360x70'	Fixed parab. and reflector			
			40'	Parab.	Equator.	R. Astro	450
9. Fort Davis	Harvard	A.F.	85'	Parab.	Equator.	R. Astro	375
10. NRL-Maryland Pt. Washington	ONR/NRL	ONR	84'	Parab.	Equator.	R. Astro	250
			50'	Parab.	Alt-Az	R. Astro	300
11. Harvard Meteor (Illinois)	NBS/H. U.	NSF		Trough	Antenna	Meteor	300
12. Cornell (Arecibo)	Cornell	ARPA	1000'	Earth bowl (Steerable feed)			4,000
						RADIO TOTALS	$23,620

Note: Costs do not include property, auxiliary instruments, or operation.

TABLE D MAJOR ASTRONOMICAL FACILITIES COMPLETED SINCE 1945 BY STATE AND PRIVATE UNIVERSITIES (No Federal Funds)

OBSERVATORY	SPONSOR	FACILITY DESCRIPTION DIA.-IN.	TYPE	MOUNT	FOR	INSTRUMENT COST ONLY AT 1963 PRICE LEVEL— $ THOUSANDS
1. Palomar Observatory	C.I.T.	200	Prime focus/ Cass/coudé	Yoke	Astron.	$ 8,500
		48/72	Schmidt	Fork	Astron.	600
2. Lick Observatory	U. Calif.	120	Cass/coudé	Fork	Astron.	2,170
3. McDonald Observatory	U. Texas U. Chicago	36	Cass	Fork	Astron.	124
4. Portage Lake Obs.	U. Mich.	24/36	Schmidt	Fork	Astron.	216
5. Washburn Observatory	U. Wis	36	Cass	Fork	Astron.	139
					Totals	$11,749

Note: Costs include: mounting, optics complete, dome and building—but not other instruments, operations or property.

TABLE E   COSTS OF LARGE RADIO ASTRONOMY PARABOLIC ANTENNAS
Steerable Mountings Above 31 Feet Dia.—Equatorial or Alt-Azimuth Mtgs.
(Revised to Jan. 1963 Costs per Price Indexes)

APERTURE DIA. FEET	MOUNT TYPE	FOR WAVE LENGTH	OBSERVATORY	MFG. BY	YEAR FAB.	1963 COSTS U.S. $ THOUSANDS
31	Alt-Az	—	Wheaton, Illinois	G. Reber	1937	1st US antenna
32	Equator	5 cm	CIT Owens Valley	CIT	1957	2.5
33	Equator	10 cm	U.C. Hat Creek, Calif.	Philco/UC	1960	4.5
40	Alt-Az	—	Air Force Tracking, Delaware, O.	Blaw Knox	1956	300
50	Alt-Az	1 cm	NRL, Wash., D.C.	Collins	1940	100
50	Alt-Az	Radar	MIT	Collins	1960	300
60	Equator	20 cm	Harvard Obs.	DS Kennedy	1956	275
60	Alt-Az	Telemetry	Commercial Telemetry	DS Kennedy	1956-60	285
83	Alt-Az	20 cm—	Bonn, Germany	Telefunken	1956	990
84	Alt-Az	—	MIT Lincoln Lab Radar	DS Kennedy	1958	460 (2)
85	Alt-Az	20 cm—	Dwingeloo, Neth.	Neth.	1957	270
85	Equator	5 cm	JPL Goldstone	Blaw Knox	1958	750
85	Equator	3 cm	AUI Green Bank, W. Va.	Blaw Knox	1959	375
85	Equator	2 cm	Univ. Michigan	Blaw Knox	1959	375
85	Equator	10 cm	U.C. Hat Creek, Calif.	Philco	1960	350
84	Equator	10 cm	NRL Maryland Pt.	DS Kennedy	1957	250
85	Alt-Az	5 cm	JPL Goldstone	Blaw Knox	1960	750
90	Equa (2)	5 cm	CIT Owens Valley	CIT/Allison	1958	970
120	Alt-Az	5 cm	MIT Lincoln Lab	NAA	1963	1,900
140	Equator	3 cm	AUI Greenbank	Stone-Webster	Const.	13,500
150	Alt-Az	long	Stanford Obs.	Soss	1959	350
150	Alt-Az	10 cm	Canada NRC	M.A.N.	Const.	2,700
210	Alt-Az	10 cm	CSIRO Australia	M.A.N. Ger.	1961	2,500
210	Alt-Az	10 cm	JPL Goldstone	Rohr	Const.	12,000
250	Alt-Az	21 cm+	Jodrell Bank	Husband	1958	5,000 to 10,000

Note: 1. Costs include mounting, erection, drive and control—no readout or R.F. equipment.
    2. Corrected costs to January 1963 based upon national average price index for equipment.
    3. This list DOES NOT INCLUDE the following antenna types: a. Steerable antennas below 30 feet diameter; b. Large radar scatter, warning systems, etc.; c. Large multiple and cluster arrays; d. Defense or classified projects.

TABLE F   TOTAL COSTS FOR LARGE OPTICAL TELESCOPES   Corrected to Jan. 1963
            From National Average Cost Index Factors for Equipment.
              Includes—Dome-Building; Telescope Mount; and Complete Optics
             Does Not Include—Land; Site Development; Observing Instruments and Auxiliaries

APERTURE INCHES	OBSERVATORY	SPONSOR	FUNDING AGENT	TELESCOPE TYPE AND MOUNTING		YEAR OPER.	COSTS OR (EST) 1963 $ THOUSANDS
16	KPNO	AURA	NSF	Cass	Off-axis	1961	(55)
18/28	Palomar	CIT/CIW	Private	Schmidt	Fork	1958	(80)
24/36	Portage Lake	U. Mich.	State	Schmidt	Fork	1958	216
24	Palomar-Mt. Whitney	CIT Lunar	NASA	Cass	Fork	Const.	25
36	KPNO	AURA	NSF	Cass	Off-axis	1960	275
36	McDonald	U. Chicago	State	Cass	Fork	1957	124
36	Washburn	U. Wis.	State	Cass	Fork	1958	139
40	Mt. Stromlo	Australia	Aus. Gov.	Cass/coudé	Off-axis	1963	350
40	European Southern	Australia Group	Aus. Gov.	Cass/coudé	Fork	Prelim.	(160)
48	Dominion Obs.	Victoria	Canada	Cass/coudé	Fork	1961	360
48/72	Palomar	CIT/CIW	Private	Schmidt	Fork	1948	675
60	U.S. Naval Obs.	Naval Obs.	USN	Cass	Fork	Const.	(1,200)
							(800 + Opt.)
60	Palomar	CIT/CIW	—	Cass/coudé	Fork	Prelim.	(650)
60	Chile Obs.	AURA	NSF	Cas/PF/coudé	Off-axis	Prelim.	(1,050)
84	KPNO	AURA	NSF	Cass/coudé	Fork	1963	(1,200)
100	Mt. Wilson	CIW		Private	Newt/Cas/cou	Yoke	1908	(1,680)
							(Old est.)
120	Lick Obs.	U.C.	State	PF/Cas/cou	Fork	1959	2,400
150	KPNO	AURA	NSF	PF/Cas/cou	Yoke	Prelim.	(3,880)
200	Palomar	CIT/CIW	Private	PF/Cas/cou	Yoke	1948	6,950

QB
33
U6N3

MAY 9 1968